RUBBER TECHNOLOGY
A Basic Course

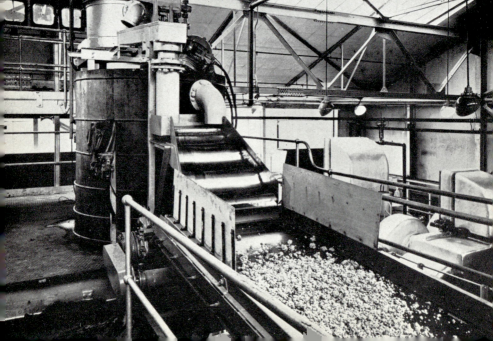

RUBBER TECHNOLOGY

A Basic Course

ALEXANDER S. CRAIG

F.I.R.I.

Rubber Technologist: India Tyre & Rubber Co. Ltd.
Senior Lecturer: Rubber Technology Dept., Stow College of
Engineering, Glasgow
Examiner in City and Guilds Course No. 120, 'Rubber
Workshop Practice'

OLIVER & BOYD
EDINBURGH AND LONDON

OLIVER AND BOYD LTD
Tweeddale Court
Edinburgh 1

39a Welbeck Street
London W. 1

First published   1963

Printed in Great Britain by Robert MacLehose and Co. Ltd
The University Press, Glasgow

DEDICATION

FOREWORD

The efficiency of an industry depends very largely on the level of understanding of the technology of that industry attained by its employees (including the management). Education raises that level of understanding, and the education of experience is most effective when based on systematic instruction in science and technology given by suitably qualified teachers.

To enable it to meet the progressive co-operation and competition encountered internationally as well as within our own country, the rubber industry requires its employees to attain high standards of proficiency in rubber technology. The Institution of the Rubber Industry (the I.R.I.) has won international recognition as the authority which defines and maintains these standards. As a matter of convenience, the I.R.I. also examines candidates in order to ascertain whether the appropriate standard of proficiency has been attained in individual cases.

The I.R.I. therefore created a Diploma Scheme having three aims, namely (i) to promote understanding of the science and technology of rubber, (ii) to encourage and approve educational facilities to meet the needs of the rubber industry, and (iii) to provide an International Examination Scheme whereby candidates sponsored by their national organisations may receive equivalent and mutually recognised awards representing the same level of attainment in the science and technology of rubber.

Of recent years, much emphasis has been laid on appropriate technological education schemes to help young people in industry. Undoubtedly, the progress of young employees will be much encouraged if they know *why* as well as *how*, and more competent candidates for promotion to technical control positions will then be available to maintain and expand the industry they serve.

The I.R.I. has met the needs of able and ambitious young recruits to the rubber industry by establishing the Licentiateship which is a Diploma designed for part-time students, to encourage those workers who have entered the rubber industry direct from school. Award of this Diploma indicates that a person is educationally qualified for a subordinate position of technical responsibility in a rubber factory.

Subsequently, the rubber industry felt the need for an award attesting successful completion of a course of instruction suitable for the worker on the rubber factory floor, for charge hands, foremen and any other workers in the industry who could improve themselves and their work by learning something of the fundamentals of rubber technology. Such a course has been sponsored by the City and Guilds of London Institute, with the encouragement and support of the Institution of the Rubber Industry, and the course is termed 'Rubber Workshop Practice'.

Successful completion of the course leads to the award of a certificate by the City and Guilds of London Institute.

This course in Rubber Workshop Practice has two very important features. No prior educational qualifications are necessary before entering the course, and the emphasis is on practical work.

I have been invited to write a foreword to Mr. Craig's book, which now makes available to a much wider circle of students the form of teaching evolved by his long and successful experience in instructing young newcomers to the rubber industry in the elements of rubber technology.

For those who are taking the Rubber Workshop Practice course, it may well serve as the principal text-book for private study and revision. The Licentiateship candidate, with higher aims and his eyes on a more distant goal, will find it a valuable introduction to rubber technology in the early stages of his course.

Mr. Craig's book is an elementary text-book but to write such a book successfully is an exacting task even for an author possessing the special qualities it demands. Every student of rubber technology has to begin by knowing nothing of the subject and needing a sound elementary introduction to it. A book like the volume here offered by Mr. Craig carries a heavy burden of responsibility. Like the humble foundation, it must carry without failure the weight of the whole building subsequently erected upon it.

As Chairman of the Education Committee and of the Examinations and Qualifications Board of the Institution of the Rubber Industry, I welcome the publication of Mr. Craig's book and thank him for the patient and unselfish labour with which he has made his own lecture notes available to all who are beginning the study of rubber technology.

Northenden, Manchester.   C. FALCONER FLINT
September, 1962.

PREFACE

This book has simply written itself rather than been written. It started some twenty years ago, shortly after the author took up the instruction of 'Rubber Trades Course' students at Stow College, Glasgow. At that time there were no suitable text-books at prices within the means of the majority of the students. The compilation of lecture notes was therefore started and, although the text-book position has improved somewhat during the past few years, a gap still exists between the 'popular' accounts of rubber and its uses, and the formidable volumes at a much higher level of instruction than is needed by the craftsman. This text aims to close that gap.

The immediate occasion of its presentation is the inauguration by the City and Guilds of London Institute, of a scheme of examinations in 'Rubber Workshop Practice'. Although most Trades Schools offering instruction in rubber technology issue their own Course Certificates, the need was felt for a National qualification. Credit is due to the Scottish Section of the Institution of the Rubber Industry for gaining the interest of the various bodies concerned and in finally having 'Rubber Workshop Practice' added to the other technologies already provided for by the City and Guilds of London Institute.

In introducing the course, the City and Guilds of London Institute say that "a scheme of examinations has been drawn up to provide a qualification in rubber workshop practice for operatives and staff employed in the rubber manufacturing industry. The syllabuses are concerned primarily with practical matters which have direct bearing on manufacturing processes, theoretical concepts being introduced only to the extent which is necessary in order to explain industrial practice. The scheme has been devised to meet the special needs both of young entrants to the industry and of older workers".

The Government's 1956 report on 'Technical Education' describes craftsmen "as representing the skilled labour of manufacturing industry and accounting for more than a third of its manpower. With the growing complexity of machines and the introduction of new materials it becomes all the more necessary for them to appreciate not only the 'how' but also the 'why' of the work they do". Many readers, be they operatives, foremen or supervisors, may never be called on to

make a rubber boot, a conveyor belt or a latex foam mattress, and it
would be a life-time's work to describe in detail the manufacture of
every rubber product from say, the humble eraser to the largest
pneumatic tyre. Your instructors will demonstrate 'how' the basic
processes of manufacture are carried out; this book deals with the
'why' — the theory for fully understanding these processes. Once they
have been carried out (perhaps on only a small scale) and the reasons
for each step precisely understood, the combination of practice and
theory may be applied to any of the various branches of the industry.
This book covers the City and Guilds' syllabus in rubber technology,
and gives guidance in selecting suitable sources of information on the
other syllabus subjects, e.g. steam supply, simple engineering drawing
and work study. The 'Reading List' goes rather beyond the syllabus
requirements, since it is hoped that it will be of assistance to those
readers who may wish to pursue their studies further.

The word 'technology' appearing in the title of this work needs
some explanation. Science may be defined briefly as classified knowledge; technology in general is the practice and description of any or
all of the applied sciences which have commercial value. Sir Lawrence
Bragg has described the difference very neatly — "Pure science is the
pursuit of knowledge the use of which is not yet clear; technology is
the exploitation of knowledge when a possible use for it becomes clear.
Pure science is the reconnaissance flight made to see what lies ahead
of us; technology is the army which advances and occupies the
ground." Rubber technology thus includes the methods by which our
raw material is obtained and by which it is transformed into articles of
commercial importance, the description of these methods with the
explanation of any specialised words used, i.e., expressions peculiar
to the industry and those which have meanings differing from ordinary
usage. The language of rubber technology has presented some difficulties in writing this text, since the terms describing several processes
vary not only between the U.K. and the U.S.A., but between different
factories in the same country. If, however, the meaning of any term is
in doubt the context should give the answer. Abbreviations are explained when first used, and the pronunciation of unfamiliar words is
given.* Suggestions for further reading will be given at the end of
each chapter. The Fahrenheit scale of temperature will be used
throughout, since most industrial equipment still employs this scale.

* The key to the pronunciation code is as follows: fāte, fär; mē, her (her); mīne,
mōte, mūte, moon.

Finally, the present author detests the phrase 'the present author' and the subject matter will be presented informally, more in the manner of workshop instruction than of lecture-hall technique. Should the reader notice an error I would be grateful if he would inform me so that the appropriate correction may be made in any future edition.

A.S.C.

ACKNOWLEDGMENTS

The preparation of this text has been made possible firstly by those responsible for my own early training in rubber technology, and secondly by those who encouraged me and assisted in the completion of the project.

Thanks are due to E. H. Ruch, former Chief Chemist of the India Tyre & Rubber Company, for first setting my feet on the 'rubber road', to J. R. M. Duncan formerly of the Craigpark Electric Cable Company who inaugurated the first Glasgow classes in rubber technology, and to Dr. J. Young, former Technical Manager of the India Tyre & Rubber Company, who kept me firmly on that rubber road, albeit rough at times, especially during the dark days of World War II.

I must acknowledge my great indebtedness to the management of the India Tyre & Rubber Company for permission to reproduce material which originally appeared in the Company's magazine, *Red Ring News*. I give sincere thanks to John Anderson, Technical Manager of the Company from 1954–1960, without whose valuable criticism and encouragement this book would not have seen the light of day. I am also grateful to the scores of students at Stow College, Glasgow, who asked searching questions, and to many old stagers of the India Tyre & Rubber Company who bore with me when I was attempting to master some of the tricks of the trade. During thirty years' study of the literature of rubber, I may have borrowed and unwittingly used here a turn of phrase, a simplified explanation, the source of which I can no longer trace. If there be any such I crave the indulgence of the original authors.

For the typing, checking and revision of the manuscript I am indebted to Mrs. H. Calvert and Mrs. T. Sorbie, and to Miss Marion Elliott for the preparation of the diagrams. For valuable criticism and advice I give thanks to Dr. F. H. Cotton and Mr. B. L. Davies of the National College of Rubber Technology, to Mr. L. L. Roe of the Moston College, Manchester (formerly Newton Heath Technical College), to Dr. C. F. Flint of the Factice Research and Development Association and to Dr. J. R. Scott and Dr. W. C. Wake of the Rubber and Plastics Research Association.

I am indebted to the following for permission to use photographs, diagrams and other material: Dunlop Rubber Co. for the frontispiece and Figs. 6, 8, 36, 37 and 39; W. & R. Chambers for the pronunciation code; Institution of the Rubber Industry for Figs. 1, 3, 4, 17 and Table VII; Natural Rubber Bureau for Figs. 2 and 7; R. T. Vanderbilt Co. Inc. New York for Figs. 9, 10, 25, 32 and permission to adapt Table IV; *Rubber and Plastics Weekly* for Figs. 11 and 55; Francis Shaw & Co. Ltd. for Figs. 15 and 22; Educational Productions Ltd. for Fig. 18; I.C.I. Ltd. for Fig. 20 and Table on p. 89; India Tyres Ltd. for Figs. 26 and 52; North British Rubber Co. for Fig. 27; Cabot Carbon Ltd. and *Encyclopaedia of Chemical Technology* (copyright by Interscience Encyclopaedia, Inc., New York) for Fig. 31; John Bright & Brothers Ltd. for Fig. 35; Textile Dept. of the Royal College of Science and Technology, Glasgow for Fig. 33; National College of Rubber Technology for Fig. 40; H. W. Wallace & Co. Ltd. for Fig. 43; Rubberware Ltd. for Fig. 44; Tensometer Ltd. for Fig. 45; R.A.P.R.A. for Figs. 46 and 47; British Standards Institution for Fig. 50; Spirax-Sarco Ltd. for Fig. 57; The British Rototherm Co. Ltd. for Fig. 59; Cambridge Instrument Co. Ltd. for Fig. 60; and Bristol's Instrument Co. Ltd. for Fig. 61. The references to British Standards are made by permission of the British Standards Institution, 2 Park St., London, W.1, from whom copies of the complete standards may be purchased.

For assistance with proof-reading I give thanks to my colleague Mr. A. McEwen.

CONTENTS

CHAPTER I

INTRODUCTION

In this preliminary chapter we will learn how rubber gets its name, what it is and why it is 'rubbery'. We will also discuss where our raw material comes from, how much is produced and how much consumed in the various branches of the rubber manufacturing industry.

The name 'Rubber'

For a material of such importance in the modern world, the term 'rubber' is extremely colourless and unscientific. It was adopted as a result of an observation made in 1770 by Joseph Priestley, a well-known chemist of the period. He said that, "I have seen a substance excellently adapted to the purpose of wiping from paper the marks of a black-lead pencil. It must therefore be of singular use to those who practise drawing. It is sold by Mr. Nairne, Mathematical Instrument Maker, opposite the Royal Exchange. He sells a cubical piece of about half-an-inch for three shillings and he says it will last several years." The new erasers must have been welcomed as a considerable improvement on the customary bread-crumbs but the high price put them in the luxury class at that time. The scientific name, caoutchouc (pronounced, kow'chook), usually reserved nowadays only for chemically purified rubber, is popularly translated from a South American dialect as the 'weeping wood', descriptive of the rubber tree showing drops or tears of the rubber-containing fluid trickling down the bark. This derivation has been questioned in recent years, and the word traced back to the culture language of the Incas, where it had the meaning of 'magician' or 'sorcerer'. As we shall see later, it is known that, in the sixth century, rubber was commonly used by the Aztecs in religious rites. The 'weeping wood' derivation has been used, however, by Vicki Baum as the title of an interesting book with rubber as its theme.

The Nature of Rubber

The two questions 'What is rubber?' and 'Why is it rubbery?' are questions of rubber science and somewhat beyond the scope of this book. However, it would be illogical to start training as a craftsman in rubber without making some attempt at answering them. First we must say just a little about atoms and molecules.

If you were in an aeroplane high over a football arena on the occasion of an International match or a Cup Final, you would see the dense crowd of spectators as a solid mass. You would have to come much lower before it was apparent that this seemingly solid mass was made up of a very large number of individual units, all pretty much alike and each capable of independent movement. So it is with matter (the scientist's name for the substances of which the universe is composed) but we do not ordinarily see this grained structure since the units or grains are very small indeed.

It is now known that the innumerable substances that make up the universe are built from ninety or so elementary substances or 'elements', the individual building brick being known as an 'atom', a name which originally meant 'not divisible'. Atom splitting is now commonplace, but when we do break up an atom of any particular element, it loses its identity and is no longer the same substance.

Returning to our football match; we know that not many of the spectators will be there entirely on their own — there will be pairs and trios of friends, coach parties, supporters' clubs, etc. So it is with atoms, which do not normally remain in the uncombined state, but form groups called 'molecules' (pronounced mol'i-kūls), the name meaning simply 'a small bit'. This much simplified explanation should make clear the text-book definitions of these terms:

An element is a substance which cannot be broken down by chemical means into simpler substances.

An atom is the smallest portion of an element that can take part in a chemical reaction.

A molecule is the smallest portion of a substance capable of existing independently and retaining the properties of that substance.

Rubber is a member of a large family of chemical substances known as hydrocarbons, since they consist solely of the elements hydrogen and carbon. The basic unit of rubber is a group consisting of five atoms of carbon and eight atoms of hydrogen, combined in a certain way. This unit is not peculiar to rubber, but is one of nature's most important standard parts, used in building up a great variety of substances. In rubber, some 5,000 of these 'isoprene' (i'sō-prēn) units, to give them their chemical name, join up end to end to form the rubber molecules. Chemists sometimes refer to rubber as 'polyiso-prene', a name which indicates this structure, the prefix 'poly' meaning 'many'. Commercial crude rubber is not pure polyisoprene, however; it contains only about 95% of rubber hydrocarbon, the remaining 5% consisting of a variety of substances of considerable importance in the subsequent factory processing of the rubber. In your study of rubber technology you will meet many other words with the prefix 'poly', the most common being 'polymer' (pol'i-mer), meaning 'made of many parts'. A 'high polymer' is one in which the molecule contains a very high number of individual units. Rubber with its 5,000 isoprene units in the molecule is a high polymer, as are many other substances in common use. The natural products wool, wood, cotton, leather, and the man-made products rayon, nylon, Terylene and 'plastics' are all high polymers.

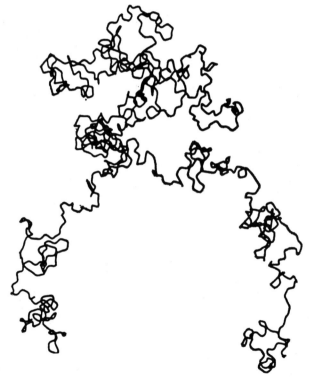

Fig. 1. Photograph of a wire model of a flexible long chain molecule.

High elasticity is one of rubber's most outstanding properties and is responsible for most of its commercial applications. Elasticity is simply the ability of a material to regain its original shape, on removal of the force which has caused the change of shape. When the isoprene units join up to form the rubber molecule, they do not assemble in straight lines but join at an angle, with the result that the complete molecule tends to coil back on itself in such a way that its ends are comparatively close together, very much closer than they would be if the molecule were unkinked. The difference is brought out very clearly in Fig. 1. A piece of rubber therefore consists of a large number of these coiled long-chain molecules, which are not themselves linked together, but are considerably entangled. If the piece of rubber is stretched, each chain will tend to straighten out, but will revert to its original shape when the stretching force is removed. It is difficult to visualise this since the dimensions involved are so very small, but if you think of a bundle of strands of woollen yarn unravelled from a knitted garment (preferably badly knitted, since the molecules are not regularly kinked) it will give you some idea of the structure. Although it may appear quite fantastic at first reading, this kinked molecule theory does explain fairly satisfactorily most of the properties of rubber-like materials.

Outline of Rubber Technology

Before we deal with the importance of the rubber industry relative to industry in general, we must discuss, very briefly at this stage, the principal features of rubber technology.

Natural rubber is obtained from a tropical tree, in the form of a milky liquid called 'latex' (lā'teks), which contains the rubber as tiny globules suspended like the droplets of fat in creamy milk. Latex is not the sap of the tree and the reason for its presence in some types of trees and vines is not known exactly. Curdling or clotting of the latex is brought about by the addition of dilute acid; the rubber globules separate out from the 'whey' or watery portion of the latex, and are arranged by partitions into rough sheets which float on top of the liquid. These sheets are washed, and dried in hot air to produce crepe rubber or dried in an atmosphere of wood smoke to produce smoked sheet rubber. With the possible exception of crepe soles for footwear, this crude rubber is not much used in the raw state; it has rather low strength, it deteriorates or 'perishes' fairly easily and it is very sensitive to quite moderate changes in temperature, becoming hard and stiff when cold, soft and sticky when warm. To overcome these serious disadvantages, which make it almost useless for commercial applications, the raw rubber is softened by kneading it between heavy rollers, and mixed with certain ingredients chosen to give the required degree of strength, stretch, resistance to abrasive wear, etc., in the manufactured article. Depending on the form which the finished article is to take, this mixed rubber may be made into thin sheets or coated on to a fabric material by the process of 'calendering'; it may be shaped to the form of a die or coated on to wire by the 'extrusion' process; the article may be made by the 'dipping' method, whereby a shaped former is dipped into a solution of rubber in a suitable solvent, or into a specially concentrated latex; the rubber may also be made into a thick dough and coated on a fabric by the 'spreading' process; again, concentrated latex may be whipped up into a froth and set in the form of a cushion or mattress in the manufacture of latex foam products. In a composite article such as a pneumatic tyre, a combination of some of these processes may be employed in the preparation of the components.

Sulphur is one of the ingredients added during the mixing process, and on subjecting this prepared rubber to heat, usually combined with pressure for shaping purposes, a chemical reaction between the rubber and the sulphur takes place. The rubber is thus transformed into a tougher, more resilient substance which has improved strength, is less liable to perish and is much less affected by heat and cold. This chemical reaction is termed 'vulcanisation', the same word being applied also to the various factory methods which bring about this reaction. The less precise term 'curing' is often used to describe these factory operations — 'press' curing, 'open steam' curing, 'hot air' curing, all of which will be described in detail later. The cured product is trimmed if necessary, inspected for flaws, suitably packaged for protection and customer appeal, and is then ready for the market.

Rubber Production and Consumption

The importance of the rubber industry to industry in general is not immediately apparent by simply comparing, on a tonnage basis, the production and consumption of rubber with the output of heavy industry; in 1959 the production of rubber for the whole world, amounting to over $3\frac{1}{2}$ million tons, was about one-seventh of the U.K. steel production for the same year. A moment's consideration will show why this comparatively small tonnage is vitally necessary for the efficient functioning of industry in general, few branches of which could operate without tyres, cables, belting or hose. In terms of human well-being, 'comfort' is a convenient term to sum up rubber's various uses; we *could* exist without rubber in the form of footwear, latex foam products, waterproofs, hot water bottles, etc., but it would certainly be a much more uncomfortable existence.

The principal rubber-producing tree is cultivated economically only in a belt extending about 700 miles on each side of the equator. This is clearly indicated in the map of South-East Asia and in Table I which shows the 1959 output of natural (tree) rubber, area by area. The figures show vividly just how serious a threat to the Allied war effort was the Japanese invasion of South-East Asia during World War II, a threat that was met and countered successfully by the almost superhuman exertions of the chemical and the rubber industries.

TABLE I

Natural Rubber Production for 1959

Source	Tonnage	
Indonesia (estates)	215,563	721,359
(smallholdings)	505,796	
Malaya (estates)	408,444	698,249
(smallholdings)	289,805	
Thailand	170,256	
Africa	141,000	
Ceylon	91,695	
Vietnam	74,183	
Sarawak	43,424	
Rest of Asia	41,750	
Cambodia	33,924	
India	23,396	
Brazil	21,109	
Rest of Latin America	7,000	
	2,067,500	

TABLE II

Synthetic Rubber Production for 1959

Type	Tonnage
S-types	1,191,957
Neoprene	124,815
Butyl	100,119
N-type	43,169
Type not specified	179,542
	1,640,000

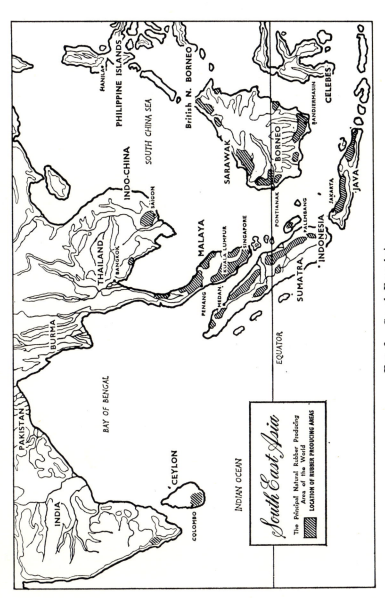

Fig. 2.   South East Asia.

TABLE III

United Kingdom Consumption, natural and synthetic for 1959

Use	Natural	Tonnage Synthetic	Total	% (approx.)
Transportation	84,090	58,169	142,259	54·9
Footwear	18,783	4,224	23,007	8·9
Cellular Rubber	16,875	58	16,933	6·5
Cables	5,973	2,399	8,372	3·2
Belting	5,841	606	6,447	2·5
Hose	3,068	1,574	4,642	1·8
Rings, seals and gaskets	2,642	1,204	3,846	1·5
Tiling and Flooring	1,483	1,020	2,503	1·0
Thread	2,239	15	2,254	0·8
Proofing	1,859	308	2,167	0·8
Surgical products	2,126	21	2,147	0·8
Ebonite	1,363	451	1,814	0·7
Sports	1,004	45	1,049	0·4
Sheeting	542	139	681	0·2
Miscellaneous	32,754	8,780	41,534	16·0
	180,642	79,013	259,655	100·0

The weights given above are British or 'long' tons of 2,240 lb., the American or short ton weighs 2,000 lb. and the French or 'metric' ton of 1,000 kg. is equivalent to 2,205 lb.

The figures in these Tables are quoted, by permission of the Secretariat of the International Study Group from the monthly publication *Rubber Statistical Bulletin.*

In addition to the natural rubber, over 1½ million tons of synthetic rubber was produced in 1959, details of which are given in Table II. As this is our first mention of synthetic rubber, it would be as well to clear up some common misconceptions right away. The word 'synthetic' is the adjective derived from the noun 'synthesis' (sin'thisis), meaning 'putting together'. The term when correctly used in its technical sense applies to the combining of two or more chemical substances to form a new substance, the process being carried out by man, in either the laboratory or the factory. The precise type of rubber made by nature in the rubber tree has not so far been synthesised by man, although we shall learn later that there are several types of synthetic polyisoprene, developed within the last few years, which come very close indeed to duplicating the structure and properties of the natural product. The term 'synthetic rubber' is therefore not strictly correct but, in spite of many other suggestions, it is the one still in common use for describing the man-made product. In this connection you may meet the word 'elastomer'. It means simply 'made of elastic parts' and was proposed some twenty years ago as a comprehensive term for any rubber-like material. The word is used quite frequently by rubber technologists but it has not yet been adopted by the general public. Using this term, tree rubber is a natural elastomer and man-made rubber is a synthetic elastomer. When the use of synthetic rubbers was suddenly forced upon us by the loss of practically all the rubber-growing areas during World War II, there was no time for the large-scale testing normally carried out on a new material, and some difficulties were experienced. At that time the general public tended to associate inferiority with the expression 'synthetic', but this misconception must now be entirely dismissed. Is it likely that $1\frac{1}{2}$ million tons would have been used in 1959 if the products were in any way inferior? As Table II shows, there are several different types of synthetic rubber, discussion of which will be left till a later chapter. Bulk production of synthetics is confined mainly to the U.S.A. and Canada, but a number of plants are now in operation in Europe, and several more are in the course of construction.

It is of interest to know how the consumption of rubber is divided among the different branches of the industry; Table III shows how some 180,000 tons of natural and 79,000 tons of synthetic rubbers were used in the United Kingdom in 1959. The proportions of rubber used by the various sections show surprisingly little change over the last ten years, with one notable exception. Cellular rubber, comprising mainly latex foam products, used only $2\frac{1}{2}\%$ of the total rubber in 1948 compared to the present $6\frac{1}{2}\%$. Transportation includes tyres, inner tubes and the materials sold for the repair and retreading of tyres, and accounts for more than half of all the rubber used in this country. If to the 'Transportation' figure we add the amounts of rubber used in vehicles in the form of engine mountings, radiator hose, floor mats, window strip, etc., the proportion taken by the motor industry approaches almost two-thirds.

The products indicated by the headings in Table III give only a hint of the extraordinary variety of the rubber industry. In the U.K. it has about 112,000 employees, the individual factories ranging from small units employing only a few operatives up to large companies or groups of companies with a pay-roll of several thousands. A few firms confine their activities to only one product or group of associated products, e.g. tyres and inner tubes, cables and electrical insulation, but most companies add to their main product a wide range of what are termed mechanical rubber goods (or simply 'mechanicals') which include hose, belting, oil-seals, gaskets, packing and the host of rubber parts used in motor vehicles. It should be noted that many rubber firms are now entering the 'plastics' field, since these materials have superseded rubber in, for example, certain types of electric cables and of conveyor belting.

REFERENCE

RUEBENSAAL, CLAYTON, F., World Synthetic Rubber — its Manufacture and Markets. *Rubb. Plast. Age.* 1961, Vol. 42, No. 10, 1196.

FIG. 3.   Rubber figures: Chichen Itza.

FIG. 4.   Rubber ball 350 years old.

CHAPTER II

A SHORT HISTORY OF THE RUBBER INDUSTRY

Early History

This most fascinating study has suffered in the past from rather fanciful accounts of its development and from the repetition of inaccuracies. We are indebted to the Institution of the Rubber Industry for commissioning, and to many eminent men in the industry for bringing to successful completion in 1952, the publication of a *History of the Rubber Industry* which has reduced these romantic accounts to proper proportions and has corrected many previously accepted inaccuracies.

It is generally considered that the first European contact with rubber was made by Christopher Columbus on his second American voyage of 1493–6, although rubber must have been known in the New World for many centuries prior to this. In the National Museum, Mexico City, there is a copy of an Aztec wall painting (the original has not survived) thought to have been made early in the sixth century, one section of which depicts a priest making an offering or sacrifice of two balls of rubber. The earliest known objects of rubber still in existence may be seen in the Peabody Museum at Harvard University, U.S.A. As will be seen from Fig. 3, they consist of small rubber figures, which were originally attached to balls of copal incense. These objects were dredged from a wishing well in the Maya city of Chichen Itza in Northern Yucatan, Mexico, and are thought to be offerings to the rain gods with whose worship the well was associated. Throughout the sixteenth century there are references to a number of games using solid rubber balls, a variety called Tlachtli, popular in ancient Mexico, being a mixture of basketball, football and hockey. It called for a considerable degree of skill since the ball, about three or four inches in diameter, had to be propelled through a stone ring not much greater in diameter. A rubber play-ball of this type, thought to be over 350 years old, is illustrated in Fig. 4. The ball was found in 1910 in the grave of a Peruvian child and may be seen in the Science Museum, South Kensington, London.

11

The first scientific study of the preparation and properties of rubber is usually attributed to a Frenchman, Charles de la Condamine, but it has recently been shown that he owed much to the work of a compatriot, Francois Fresneau, who discovered in 1747 the variety of rubber tree known as 'Hevea brasiliensis'. This variety is nowadays the principal rubber-producing tree, having, as the botanical name indicates, its original home in Brazil. Fresneau describes in great detail the native methods of manufacture — spreading latex on cloth to make it waterproof, and forming hollow vessels of rubber by coating a clay mould with latex, drying over a smoky fire, crushing the clay and removing it through the neck of the vessel.

Unless a preservative is added to fresh latex it soon coagulates of its own accord. The discovery that the addition of an alkaline substance would prevent this spontaneous coagulation was made about 1790, but was not applied until quite recent times. Very little liquid latex was therefore available in Europe for experiment, and efforts were accordingly directed towards finding a solvent for the solid rubber. Turpentine, ether and petroleum were all in use towards the end of the eighteenth century, but their high cost prevented their general adoption. In 1818, James Syme, a Scottish medical student, discovered that the light spirit distilled from coal tar was as efficient a solvent for rubber as petroleum spirit. This coal tar naphtha could be produced quite cheaply since it was a by-product in the manufacture of coal gas, then becoming popular for illumination. Charles Macintosh, a Glasgow chemical manufacturer who supplied the textile mills of the district with dyestuffs, required a cheap and plentiful source of ammonia in his business. He was naturally interested in the crude ammonia liquor which was being produced in the newly started Glasgow Gas Works, and he eventually contracted to take the complete range of by-products. The ammonia he used himself in dyestuff manufacture, the heavier oil distilled from the coal tar and the coal tar pitch itself were sold profitably, but no buyer could be found for the naphtha. Macintosh eventually employed it himself to make a rubber solution which he spread on one side of a fabric, two plies of which were pressed together, rubbered sides adjacent, to form the first macintosh waterproof cloth. Production was started at Campsie, near Glasgow, in 1823, and was so successful that a move was made in the following year to much larger premises in Manchester.

Thomas Hancock, a London coach-builder, first became interested in rubber in 1819. He discovered the main methods of rubber manufacture and, on this account, is sometimes called 'the father of the rubber industry'. At this period rubber was imported in the form of rough bottles, which Hancock cut into strips to make gloves, shoe soles, braces, garters, etc. He devised a method of using up the scrap pieces by working them in a machine which we would now call an internal mixer but which Hancock referred to as a 'pickle', with the object of keeping its true purpose a secret. This device consisted of a

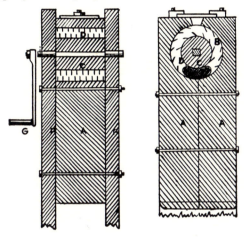

Fig. 5. Hancock's pickle.

spiked roll working inside a spiked hollow cylinder, the roll having a crank operated by hand. By doing work on raw rubber it becomes soft and self-adhesive, and, after pressing in a mould, the product of Hancock's pickle gave a solid block of rubber much easier to cut and make up than the original bottles. This first model held about one pound of rubber, but the largest size of 'single-roll masticator', Hancock's later development of the same principle, produced blocks of rubber weighing 180 to 200 lb. It was found that this masticated rubber dissolved much more easily in solvent than the unplasticised material, giving a more concentrated solution. Macintosh quickly appreciated the advantages of this, and soon came to an agreement with Hancock to use his process.

As early as 1825 Hancock was granted a patent for the manufacture of rubberised cloth which involved passing the rubber and cloth between a pair of rollers, but the invention of the two-roll mill and of the calender is generally credited to an American, Edwin M. Chaffee, who described these basic processing machines in 1836. In the following year Hancock invented the spreading machine, an apparatus for coating fabric with rubber 'dough', from which the solvent is evaporated leaving a film of rubber on the cloth. There is some doubt as to the origin of the forcing machine or extruder. A piston type, operating in the manner of a domestic cake icing set, is known to have been in use for extruding rubber on to hose in 1856, but it was not until 1880 or thereabouts that the screw-operated machine was first developed by the firms of Shaw in England and Royle in America.

The Discovery of Vulcanisation

More has been written on this subject than on any other aspect of rubber history and even now it is not possible to state definitely who was the discoverer of the process of vulcanisation. In the early 1830's many scientists were seeking a 'cure' for rubber's unfortunate susceptibility to quite moderate changes in temperature. The return of footwear which became rock-hard in cold weather and of raincoats which softened and fell off their hangers in hot weather was rapidly ruining rubber manufacturers, for it must be remembered that prior to the discovery of vulcanisation, hundreds of types of articles, ranging from beer hose to air pillows, were being made from raw rubber. The use of sulphur keeps cropping up in the reports of these experiments — sulphur dusted on the surface of rubber, rubber dissolved in solvents to which sulphur had been added, etc., but the credit for the discovery of vulcanisation by means of heating a rubber-sulphur mixture is given to the American, Charles Goodyear. Success came in 1839 after many years of painstaking work and several grievous disappointments. Goodyear did not patent his discovery until 1844, whereas Hancock obtained a British Patent for a process of vulcanisation in 1843, admitting quite openly that he had seen samples of sulphur-vulcanised rubber, probably made by Goodyear. 'Metallic gum-elastic' was the name given by Goodyear to his 'cured' rubber, but the process was soon given the modern term 'vulcanisation' a word first suggested by William Brockedon of the Macintosh Co. The name is quite an apt one, since Vulcan, the mythical god of fire, who had his workshops in volcanic mountains, would be very familiar with both heat and sulphur.

A method of vulcanisation without the necessity of heating, the 'cold cure' process, was discovered in 1846 by Alexander Parkes of Birmingham, who found that thin strips of raw rubber immersed in a solution of sulphur chloride diluted by carbon disulphide were very quickly vulcanised. Since only fairly thin articles may be vulcanised by the cold cure method, it finds its most important application in the production of proofed fabrics.

Development of the Plantation Industry

After the discovery of vulcanisation the demand for rubber increased considerably and it was soon apparent that the manufacturing industry could not rely solely on rubber obtained from trees growing wild in tropical jungles. The Brazilian authorities, having a monopoly of the best type of wild rubber — Para rubber, named after the town at the mouth of the Amazon from which it was exported — raised the price to a very high level. In Africa, the treatment of the native tribes collecting rubber aroused world-wide indignation. Wild rubber trees were generally 'slaughter-tapped', the term indicating that the maximum amount of latex is taken in the shortest possible time, with no regard for the welfare of the trees or future supplies of latex. For these reasons cultivation of a suitable rubber tree became imperative. After several failures, success was achieved in 1876 by Sir Henry Wickham, who collected some 70,000 seeds of the Hevea tree in Brazil and brought them to Kew Gardens, where about 2,600 germinated. The resulting seedlings were sent to Ceylon, India and Malaya and thus the plantation industry was founded. It would have taken very much longer indeed to establish the plantations without the strenuous efforts of H. N. Ridley, who died as recently as 1956 in his one hundred and first year. He distributed Hevea seed, encouraged the first planters, taught them how to control diseases to which the trees were subject and, most important of all, discovered a method of tapping which enables the latex to be obtained without hacking the trees to death. Plantation rubber was first marketed about 1900 and production increased steadily at the expense of wild rubber, which is now of little importance except in times of emergency.

Invention of the Pneumatic Tyre

In 1845 R. W. Thomson was granted a patent for a tyre embodying an air-inflated inner tube and an outer cover. Although these 'aerial wheels' were successfully used on horse-drawn carriages, the comparatively slow speed did not show off the advantages of the pneumatic principle and Thomson's work was overlooked for many years.

In 1888 J. B. Dunlop, who was unaware of the earlier patent, developed a similar type of tyre which he tried out on a bicycle. Here the advantages in speed and comfort over the existing solid tyre were immediately apparent and the pneumatic principle then received general acceptance. Cord fabric for the casings of tyres was introduced about 1916 and soon superseded the closely woven fabrics then in use. The reinforcing effect and improved resistance to abrasion obtained by incorporating carbon black (a special kind of soot) into rubber had been known from 1904, but it was little used in tyres until the improved cord casing demanded a longer wearing tread portion.

A great deal of the technical progress in the rubber industry has resulted from the necessity of obtaining longer tyre life. In service, a tyre has to withstand a combination of forces, such as abrasion, flexing, etc., all tending to its destruction — a motorcar tyre running at 30 m.p.h. receives about seven deflections every second during its life of approximately 20,000 miles. Advantage has been taken of developments in compounding which produce rubbers giving good service under these conditions, e.g. carbon black for abrasion resistance, accelerators to increase the efficiency of the vulcanisation reaction and thus improve quality, and antioxidants to resist premature perishing. Since tyre manufacture uses such immense quantities of rubber, it has largely originated the developments in the large-scale use of machinery, which have often subsequently been adopted in other branches of the industry where applicable.

Synthetic Rubber

Research on the structure of any material usually involves breaking it down into its constituent parts (analysis) and then building it up again from similar parts to check the result (synthesis). This was attempted with rubber from about 1860 onwards without any thought of the commercial applications of a synthetic rubber-like material. As the industry progressed, however, several reasons emerged which finally led to the large-scale production of such materials. Firstly, natural rubber was found to be almost useless for any application in which it came into contact with oil; then, the wide fluctuations in the price of natural rubber proved very irksome to manufacturers; and finally, the concentration of rubber-growing in South-East Asia stimulated research on synthetic rubber in those countries which, for a variety of reasons, did not wish to be dependent on the natural product.

Towards the end of World War I, Germany was producing a very poor quality synthetic material, 'methyl rubber', the supply of natural rubber having been practically stopped by the Allied blockade. Research was continued vigorously and about 1930 a much more satisfactory material (called Buna S), was developed. This was a similar type of rubber to the synthetic elastomer which was rushed into production in the U.S.A. during World War II, after the majority of the world's natural rubber growing areas were occupied by the Japanese.

The synthetic rubbers so far mentioned are general-purpose types, i.e. they will replace natural rubber in most applications. Special-purpose synthetics are those which are superior to natural rubber in some particular property. Two of these special-purpose materials, Neoprene and Thiokol, which have much better resistance to the action of oils and solvents than has natural rubber, were first put on the market in 1931 and 1932 respectively and continue in use up to the present time. Butyl rubber, discovered in 1937, has much better air-holding qualities than natural, while silicone rubber, commercially available from 1944, is noted for its resistance to extremes of heat and cold. Within the last few years there has been produced what might almost be termed a true synthetic rubber — a man-made product having properties almost identical to those of the product of the Hevea tree. Although it is known by various trade names, we will refer to it meantime by its chemical name, synthetic polyisoprene.

This brief historical note will suffice for the general reader, but the technician would do well to remember that completely new inventions and processes are rare in our industry and he will find much of interest in the personal narratives of Hancock, Goodyear and the other pioneers of the rubber industry.

REFERENCES

P. SCHIDROWITZ, T. R. DAWSON (Editors), *History of the Rubber Industry* Cambridge.

RIDLEY, H. N., Evolution of the Rubber Industry. *Proc. Inst. Rubber Ind.*, 1955, Vol. 2, 114.

CHAPTER III

THE PREPARATION OF RAW RUBBER

Para Rubber

As we have seen, this is natural rubber obtained from 'wild' jungle trees and is of little commercial importance at the present time. It is, however, of some historical interest for, as late as 1920, the best quality of Para (pa-rá) rubber (known as 'Fine Hard Para') was the standard by which the newer plantation rubbers were judged, and even in 1941, an American company said they preferred Para to plantation rubber for cable insulation. In addition, the primitive method of preparation has some features of technical importance which account for the excellent reputation of Para rubber.

The latex is obtained by making a V-shaped cut in the bark of the tree and is collected in a small cup stuck on the tree at the base of the cut. The contents of a large number of cups are transferred to a larger vessel, and the rubber is obtained by a combined coagulation and smoking process. A wooden paddle is dipped into the latex and then rotated slowly in the smoke from a wood fire. The acids in the smoke coagulate the rubber globules in the latex, while some of the liquid drops off the paddle and the remainder is evaporated by the heat. When the first layer of rubber is quite dry, the paddle is given a fresh coat of latex and the drying process repeated. There is thus built up a large ball of rubber, termed a 'biscuit', weighing anything from 25 to 100 lb., which is cut in half and stripped from the paddle. The beneficial effect of the addition to rubber of carbon black (a special form of soot) has already been mentioned, and in this laborious method of preparing Para rubber we have an example of its almost accidental use. Since each thin layer of rubber was dried individually in a smoky flame the proportion of carbon particles was much higher than in plantation rubber. This could well explain the fact that, prior to the development of modern compounding, Para rubber was considered by many manufacturers to be superior to the more lightly smoked plantation product.

Fig. 6. Tapping a rubber tree.

Plantation Rubber

This term includes all natural rubber obtained from cultivated trees, but it must be remembered that production from Malaya and Indonesia is roughly divided equally between large estates, mostly European-controlled, and small-holdings operated by native families. The bulk of the world production of natural rubber is obtained from a species of tree which has the botanical name 'Hevea brasiliensis'. As the second part of the name indicates, the Hevea (hev'ē-a) tree was found originally only in Brazil, in the Amazon valley of South America, but it is now established in South-East Asia which has the combination of high temperature and high rainfall suitable for its most efficient growth. Although numerous attempts have been made, it is only within the last few years that the Hevea tree has been successfully established on a plantation basis in its native home.

The usual method of starting a plantation is to fell all the trees and burn off most of the undergrowth. Seeds from a rubber tree are then planted either on the site itself, or are first started off in nursery beds and the young trees later transferred to their final positions. Using ordinary unselected seed the annual output of rubber is only about 400 lb. per acre, but nowadays seed is usually selected from trees which are known to give a high latex yield. As the present trees are replaced by the high yielding types, output is expected to reach about 1,000 lb. per acre. Families of trees descended from a proved high yielding tree are known as 'clones', and an effective way of increasing such a family, and thus increasing the plantation output, is by the gardener's practice of grafting. A piece of wood bearing a living bud from the high yielding tree is grafted on to a year-old plant raised from ordinary seed. The young tree then grows up with the good qualities of the parent.

The density of planting is about 200 per acre, the trees being about 15 ft. apart, although loss by disease and wind damage gradually reduces the numbers to about 100 productive trees per acre. A cover crop of a harmless weed is usually established while the trees are young, to compact the soil and prevent it being washed away by the heavy rainfall. Proper drainage is important and on a hilly site it may be necessary to build up the ground in a series of terraces.

'Tapping' is the name given to the cutting of the tree to allow the latex to flow out. It is hardly the most apt term since it rather infers that a gush of latex follows the incision in the bark. Actually only a few ounces of latex are obtained at each tapping, a single 224 lb. bale of rubber representing the yearly output of about thirty trees. The tapper uses a specially-shaped knife (Fig. 6) to make an initial $\frac{1}{4}$ in. deep cut in the bark. The bottom of the cut, which runs downwards from left to right at an angle of about 30°, is shaped into a groove

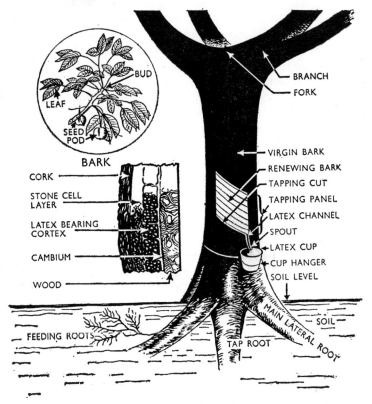

Fig. 7.   Diagram of a rubber tree.

from which a shaving of bark about $\frac{1}{25}$ in. thick is removed in subsequent tappings. The latex flows down the groove until it meets a vertical channel where a spout guides it into the collecting cup (Fig. 7), to which a small amount of an anti-coagulant has previously been added. Opinions differ as to the tapping system which will give the greatest yield of latex, but at the same time permit the bark to renew itself before that area is again tapped. A popular method is to tap every other day, the cut extending over one-third of the circumference of the tree. Tapping is started when the tree is from five to seven years old and a healthy tree will give a good yield for about forty years. The tapper sets to work early in the morning so that he may avoid the fierce mid-day heat; on his first visit he makes the tapping cut on his 'task' of about 300 trees and on his second visit, by which time the flow of latex has ceased, he empties it from the collecting cups into a larger vessel for transport to the estate factory.

Here the latex is strained to remove any particles of bark, dirt or small lumps of coagulated rubber, and is blended with latex from other parts of the plantation with the object of smoothing out the unavoidable variations in quality. The rubber content of the latex varies from 30% to 45%, depending on the season of the year. As a constant rubber content is desirable prior to coagulation, the actual rubber content is determined by either actually coagulating a small sample of the latex and weighing the rubber obtained, or by taking the specific gravity of the latex by means of a hydrometer and consulting a table showing the corresponding rubber content. The latex is then diluted with water to give a concentration of about 15% if the product is to be smoked sheet, or about 20% if crepe rubber is to be made. After standing for some time to allow any remaining fine dirt to settle on the bottom of the tank, the latex is passed into the tanks in which coagulation is carried out. A dilute solution of either acetic or of formic acid is added, thoroughly mixed in and aluminium divisions inserted in grooves in the sides of the tank to divide the coagulating rubber into slabs. When coagulation is complete (the process is usually allowed to continue overnight) the slabs are washed in water, stuck together at the ends to form a continuous band and floated down a channel to the sheeting mills. Rubber 'mills' will be described in detail later, but if you visualise a heavy mangle with the rollers set side by side instead of one above the other you will get the idea for the moment. For the production of smoked sheet rubber, the slabs are again washed and then passed in turn through five or six mills with smooth rolls and through a final mill which engraves the rubber with a ribbed design, often incorporating the name of the plantation. After draining, the sheets are hung in an atmosphere of smoke produced by burning wood, the process taking three or four days. The smoking process may sometimes be omitted, the rubber being then marketed as 'air-dried sheet'. For crepe rubber production the slabs are given much more severe treatment, being passed ten or fifteen times through a series of mills the rolls of which are grooved and are turning at slightly different speeds. During its passage through the rollers a stream of water is played on the rubber to wash out any liquid remaining from the coagulation process. Drying is done in air at the normal temperature of about 100° F and takes a week or ten days. Extreme care is necessary at all stages of the preparation of first latex crepe rubber if the desirable pale colour is to be retained. Crepe rubber for shoe soling is made by plying up the single sheets (about 0·040 in. thick) to thicknesses of $\frac{1}{8}$ in., $\frac{3}{16}$ in. or $\frac{1}{4}$ in.

Ribbed smoked sheet (usually abbreviated to R.S.S.) is marketed by assembling the single sheets into a package or 'bale' of either 224 or 250 lb., measuring roughly 24 in. × 20 in. × 20 in. A bale of 70 lb. is now available and is preferred by many manufacturers since it is more easily handled than the standard bale, and may often be processed without splitting into smaller portions. Crepe rubbers are obtainable in bales of either 224 or 180 lb. The usual pre-war covering for a bale of rubber was a plywood case, but 'bare-back' packing is now generally accepted, the bale being encased in a wrapper of the same quality rubber, which may be removed or not before processing, depending on the end-product.

There are six market grades of Ribbed Smoked Sheet, ranging from No. 1X R.S.S. European Estates through Nos. 1, 2, 3, 4 and 5, the quality, judged on appearance only, dropping slightly as the numbers increase. Crepe is of four main types, Pale Crepe, Estate Brown Crepe, Blanket Crepe and Flat Bark Crepe, with a considerable number of varieties within each type. The manufacture of Pale Crepe has been described above. Estate Brown is of excellent quality although it is based on the rubber coagulated naturally on the estate, mainly the little pieces of rubber removed from the tree before the tapper makes a fresh cut, and the pre-coagulated lumps strained from the latex before it is processed. Blanket Crepes are the so-called 'remilled' grades, usually the produce of small-holders, since the sheeting is not completed immediately after coagulation, the wet slabs being shipped to a central factory for processing. Flat Bark Crepe is the lowest crepe grade; it is made from earth scrap, rubber resulting from the coagulation of latex which has fallen on the ground, and from any other scrap which has been exposed to sunlight and has thus become very tacky. The output of a typical plantation comprises about 85% of first grade rubber, either Smoked Sheets or Pale Crepe, 10% of Brown Crepe and 5% of Flat Bark Crepe.

Rubber is a natural product and in spite of all the precautions taken on the estates, quite wide variations can occur in two properties of extreme importance in factory operations, viz., plasticity and rate of vulcanisation. Varying plasticity means that different shipments of rubber require different treatment to bring them to the 'workability' specified for the process, while variation in curing rate may require modification to time and temperature of vulcanisation to give the same properties in the product. A scheme for the testing of sample bales on the plantation, and the marking of each bale with a simple code to indicate whether it has high, medium or low plasticity and is slow, medium or fast curing has been introduced within the last ten years. The plasticity grading was found to be unreliable and has now been discontinued. Rubber which has been classified in this way is termed Technically Classified (T.C.) rubber.

A modified type of natural rubber which has certain desirable qualities in processing, particularly in calendering and extrusion, has recently been put on the market. It is aptly named Superior Processing Rubber, or simply SP rubber, and is produced on the plantation by the addition of a quantity of vulcanised latex. (As we shall see later it is possible to vulcanise rubber latex without destroying its liquid form). In the case of SP Smoked Sheet the vulcanised latex is added to the normal latex which is then coagulated and worked up into the usual sheet. This method is not possible for the production of SP Brown Crepe, since this grade is made from pre-coagulated rubber and is never available in latex form. Brown Crepe is given the SP properties by blending with it, at the washing stage, a quantity of a rubber prepared from a latex which has a much higher proportion of vulcanised latex added earlier, in other words, an SP masterbatch. The proportions of crepe and masterbatch are chosen so that the resulting SP crepe will have the same improved processing qualities as the other SP grades.

Other Natural Rubbers

Although hundreds of plants are known to contain a small percentage of rubber, only two are of commercial importance, the 'guayule' (gwä-ū'-lä) shrub and the 'kok-saghyz' or Russian dandelion. These do not require a tropical climate and are therefore of interest to those countries who wish to be independent of the usual rubber-growing areas. Guayule rubber was originally a wild rubber obtained from a shrub which is a native of Mexico, but it has been cultivated on a plantation basis, as an alternative source of natural rubber. The rubber is not obtained by tapping, but by harvesting the plants, crushing them and washing out the woody fibre. The common British dandelion contains about $\frac{1}{2}\%$ of rubber, but the kok-saghyz variety, originally grown in Russia, may contain as much as 10%. The extraction of the rubber is somewhat similar to the extraction of sugar from beet. Many countries have made extensive tests of kok-saghyz rubber since it is of excellent quality and the output per acre compares favourably with that of plantation rubber.

Gutta-percha, Balata and Chicle

Although these materials are not really rubbers, their use is usually considered part of the rubber industry, and they are mentioned here for the sake of completeness.

Gutta-percha, balata and chicle have the same chemical composition as rubber, i.e. the unit contains five carbon atoms and eight hydrogen atoms, but the way the atoms are arranged in the molecule varies from that of rubber hydrocarbon.

Gutta-percha is hard at ordinary temperatures, but becomes quite plastic on gentle heating. On recooling it sets to its original condition, and this heating and cooling may be carried out indefinitely without much deterioration. Although it can be obtained in latex form by tapping certain trees, it is now extracted by mechanical means from the prunings and leaves of the gutta-percha bush. Its principal use was for the insulation of submarine telegraph cables, but it has been superseded to a large extent in this application by the plastic material polythene (chemically, polyethylene).

Balata is very similar to gutta-percha and may be used as a substitute for it in most applications. Its best known use is in the manufacture of belting. It is obtained in latex form, the tapping method being much more severe than for rubber, since the trees can rarely be tapped a second time.

Chicle is derived from a latex-yielding plant, the product being used almost entirely as the basis of chewing gum.

REFERENCES

Vanderbilt Rubber Handbook. 1958, New York, U.S.A., pp. 13–39.
HORRIDGE, F. R., *The Trade in Natural Rubber.* Purchasing Officers Association, London.
Natural Rubber Grades and Contracts. Federation of British Rubber and Allied Manufacturers, London.

CHAPTER IV

SYNTHETIC RUBBERS AND RUBBER DERIVATIVES

Brief references to synthetic rubbers have been made already — production and consumption in Chapter I and history of development in Chapter II. Now we must look at the manufacture and uses of these materials in greater detail.

We already know that synthetic elastomers, fibres and plastics all belong to that class of substances termed 'high polymers', since their molecules consist of a large number of simple molecular units joined together in the manner of the links of a chain. Such polymers are formed as the result of complex reactions between organic chemicals under conditions requiring the highest degree of chemical engineering skill; it is therefore difficult to keep the description of their manufacture at technician level. The distinction between organic and inorganic chemistry is explained in Chapter V, and, as mentioned in a previous chapter, it must again be emphasised that, to the chemist, the word 'synthetic' does not mean 'inferior' or 'imitation', but signifies that the product is man-made and scientifically identical in all respects to the natural product. The technologist uses the word more loosely, 'synthetic rubber' being an omnibus term for all synthetic rubber-like materials. It has already been stressed that natural rubber, comprising some 95% rubber hydrocarbon and 5% non-rubber constituents, has not been exactly synthesised.

We know from the popular Press that these high polymers derive from raw materials such as water, coal, air, limestone and salt, and the inference may be drawn that some magic is involved in producing here a rubber, there a fibre. Magic to the layman maybe, but the student must realise that the infinite variety of synthetic substances results from a series of reactions, first worked out painstakingly but logically in the laboratory, then put on a pilot plant basis, and finally transferred to full-scale factory production. It is true, however, that some modern synthetic materials have resulted from an astute chemist taking a second look at the properties of an apparently unwanted product of his research.

Synthetic rubbers of various types have been accepted by industry for many years in their own right, and not simply as rubber-like materials to be used only because the natural product was not available. It is therefore nowadays difficult to credit the scorn with which the early announcements of the alleged production of synthetic rubbers were received, so convinced were the natural rubber producers of its impossibility. One writer referring, in 1908, to a product made at Burton-on-Trent notes that "from the published formula it would seem to be equal parts of old Burton ale and offensive smell".

We have already noted how the various kinds of synthetics are divided somewhat arbitrarily, into general purpose types and special purpose types, the former being used as a general replacement for natural rubber and the latter having some property or combination of properties which makes them suitable for a particular application. It should now be obvious that no one elastomer has all the desirable properties. The first commercial production was of the very poor quality methyl rubber, made of necessity in Germany during World War I. One of natural rubber's shortcomings — its poor resistance to oils and solvents — limited its application in the mechanical field but in the early 1930's two oil-resisting synthetic rubbers were put on the market — Neoprene (originally called 'Duprene') and Thiokol. As part of the preparations for World War II, German scientists had intensified their efforts to produce a satisfactory synthetic and in the middle 1930's it was announced that Germany was no longer dependent on supplies of natural rubber. The new rubbers were Buna S and Buna N types, now known as styrene-butadiene and nitrile rubbers respectively. About this time Russia also announced the production of SKA and SKB, both polybutadiene, a type of synthetic in which interest has been revived in recent years. Although World War II broke out in 1939 it was not until mid-1941 and early 1942 that a slow start was made in the U.S.A. in producing a synthetic of the Buna S type. Once the urgency of the situation was realised, the chemical industry carried out the extraordinary feat of laying down plant and increasing production to about 800,000 tons annually in the short space of two years. This rubber was mostly SBR, called at that time GR-S (Government Rubber-Styrene), since it was made under U.S. Government auspices. Butyl rubber, first announced in 1937, was found to be much less permeable to the passage of gases than natural rubber and was the obvious replacement for such uses as pneumatic tyre inner tubes, when the natural product was no longer available. U.S.A. production of neoprene and of nitrile rubbers also increased about this time to meet the growing demand for elastomers of all kinds. In 1942 Canada started production of synthetic rubber from a Government factory at Sarnia, Ontario. Silicone rubber, noted for its resistance to extremes of temperature, was available in 1944.

The polymers mentioned above — SBR, neoprene, butyl, nitrile and silicone rubbers — are those in bulk commercial production. Due to the increasing severity of the conditions to which elastomers are subjected, research has been intensified, particularly during the last ten years, and there is now available in pilot plant quantities a whole host of special purpose polymers. The most interesting development in recent years was the announcement in 1955 of the production of synthetic polyisoprene — a polymer with a chemical structure identical to that of natural rubber and, it is claimed, with all its good processing qualities.

The fact that little mention has been made of modern synthetic rubber production outside the U.S.A. and Canada is a direct result of World War II, the plants being located there for safety. In most other countries plants are now in production or in course of erection (seven in the U.K. alone) and older plants are being rebuilt and extended to take full advantage of the recent advances in manufacturing techniques.

Reference has already been made to the extremely bewildering nomenclature of synthetic rubbers. The student would only be confused by any attempt to list chemical names, the corresponding code numbers and each individual manufacturer's brand name — information which is readily available in the literature. Below are given the abbreviations recently recommended by the American Society for Testing and Materials (A.S.T.M.) in naming the rubber group of elastomers. Only one of these (SBR) is in common use, but some of the others have been seen in the literature within the past few years.

BR Butadiene rubbers	NBR Nitrile-butadiene rubbers
IR Isoprene rubbers synthetic	NCR Nitrile-chloroprene rubbers
CR Chloroprene rubbers	PBR Pyridine-butadiene rubbers
NR Isoprene rubber, natural	SBR Styrene-butadiene rubbers
ABR Acrylate-butadiene rubbers	SCR Styrene-chloroprene rubbers
IIR Isobutylene-isoprene rubbers	SIR Styrene-isoprene rubbers

In the manufacture of high polymers, the process of building up the simple units into long molecular chains is termed 'polymerisation'. The common synthetic rubbers are produced by carrying out the polymerisation in a liquid medium — emulsion polymerisation — the resulting latex being coagulated and the solid rubber obtained. The above list shows that many synthetic rubbers are made from two organic components, the 'monomers', which are intimately mixed at an early stage in manufacture and then polymerised together, the process being termed 'co-polymerisation'. It might be thought that it would be simpler to carry out the polymerisation of each monomer in turn and later combine the polymers in definite proportions. This method does not give the desired result, however; the properties of styrene-butadiene rubber would not be obtained by attempting to blend together the requisite proportions of polystyrene (a hard glass-like plastic), and polybutadiene (a very tough elastomer), once the monomers have been separately polymerised.

Styrene-Butadiene Rubber (SBR)

The two organic liquids are mixed in the proportions of approximately 25% styrene and 75% butadiene, made into an emulsion and then charged into the reaction vessels where the polymerisation takes place. The reaction is brought about by a 'catalyst', a substance which speeds up a chemical reaction, and stopped by another chemical (the 'short-stop') when about 60% of the monomers have polymerised. There are two main reasons for stopping the reaction at this stage — it is at this point that the reaction begins to slow down considerably and at approximately 60% conversion the resultant rubber has the required processability. In the early days of GR-S manufacture the reaction temperature was about 120° F but towards the end of World War II the discovery of very active catalyst systems enabled the reaction temperature to be lowered to 41° F without any increase in reaction time. Lowering the temperature brings about a change in the molecular structure of the co-polymer which considerably improves its physical properties, giving, among other things, increased tread life of tyres. The rubber resulting from the lower temperature polymerisation was called Low Temperature Polymer (LTP), once popularly referred to as 'cold' GR-S, to distinguish it from the original polymer made at 120° F which was given the designation 'hot' GR-S.

After removal of the unreacted styrene and butadiene an anti-oxidant is added to what we might now call the SBR latex, which is then coagulated in a manner similar to that for natural rubber latex, the coagulants being dilute sulphuric acid and brine (common salt) solution. The process is completed by removal of the serum, washing, drying and packing of the rubber, the bale being the easily handled one of 80 lb. By adjusting the polymerisation reaction to produce a rubber of higher molecular weight (which would of itself result in processing difficulties) and adding at the latex stage 25 to 30 PHR of an oil extender, we obtain a rubber very similar in properties to LTP but at a lower cost, the added oil being cheaper than either styrene or butadiene. This is Oil Extended Polymer (OEP) also referred to as SBR/oil masterbatch.

In discussing the processing, curing and applications of the synthetic rubbers mentioned in this chapter we can speak only in general terms — detailed information regarding compounding and applications will be found in manufacturers' literature, while the student will receive instruction in processing on workshop equipment. In transferring a new synthetic from laboratory to full scale factory production, the technician should not adhere too rigidly to the published processing details. Given the co-operation of the key men on mixing, calendering and extruding, it is surprising just how soon their existing 'know-how' is applied to the new polymer. Older technologists will remember the difficulties attendant on the return to natural rubber after World War II, with operatives accustomed only to GR-S, butyl and neoprene.

The compounding and processing of SBR follows natural rubber practice, except that greater acceleration is needed since SBR is rather slower curing. An important difference is that the 'pure gum' tensile strength of SBR is low, reinforcing fillers being needed to give serviceable products. SBR may be used in most applications where natural rubber is employed, with one notable exception — the treads of large truck and bus tyres where the lower resilience of SBR leads to greater heat build-up and excessive running temperatures.

Neoprene

This is the name given to a large family of polymers based on the organic chemical, chloroprene. They are prepared by emulsion polymerisation, the method being similar to that used for the manufacture of SBR. The chemicals used in the process — emulsifier, catalyst, modifier, short-stop and stabiliser — are varied according to the particular type of neoprene being made. The resulting latex is coagulated and the film of rubber is twisted to form a 'rope', which is later cut into short rods.

Products made from neoprene have good resistance to 'weathering'. Neoprene compounds, in common with most other organic substances, will burn when a high temperature flame is applied, but do not support combustion once the flame is removed. This property of non-flammability makes neoprene the preferred polymer for the cover stocks of underground conveyor belting in coal mines in some countries, although in the U.K. PVC has been standardised for this application.

The types of neoprene in common use are the G family (GN, GNA and GRT) and the W family (W and WRT). The curing system varies with the type but in general sulphur is not needed, the curatives being zinc oxide and magnesium oxide. A special grade of the latter — calcined magnesia, neoprene grade — should be used to ensure freedom from scorching. A typical 'base' compound, i.e. one containing no filler loading, is as follows:

Neoprene GN	100·0
Light calcined magnesia	4·0
Zinc oxide	5·0
Antioxidant	2·0
Stearic acid	0·5
MBTS	0·5

Butyl Rubber

The raw materials for the manufacture of butyl rubber are isobutylene and isoprene. They are both products of petroleum refining. The isobutylene is mixed with 2% to 3% of isoprene, diluted with methyl chloride and cooled to about $-140°$ F. The catalyst is also dissolved in methyl chloride, added continuously to the isobutylene-isoprene mixture and thoroughly dispersed. The process differs from the manufacture of other synthetics in that there is no latex stage, the polymer being formed as a coarse slurry in which the tiny particles rapidly grow larger until they form a rough crumb. After removal of any isobutylene and isoprene which have not reacted the crumb is dried, milled and packaged.

Butyl rubber is available with several different rates of cure and in various Mooney viscosities. In general all grades process similarly to natural rubber, but greater acceleration and higher curing temperatures are needed. Butyl rubber must not be contaminated with natural rubber or SBR, and softeners such as pine tar and rosin should be avoided since all these materials seriously retard the rate of vulcanisation. Treatment of butyl with bromine or chlorine, giving

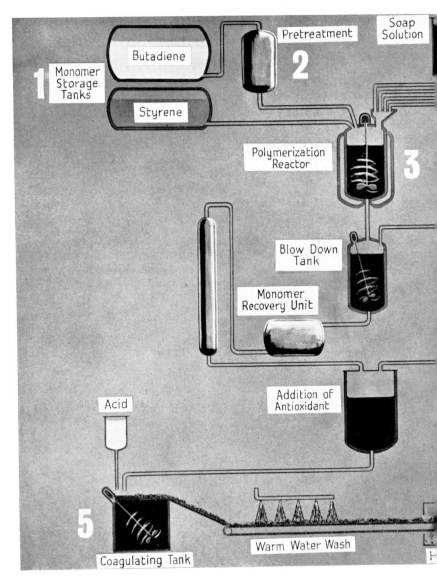

FIG. 8.   SBR manufacture.

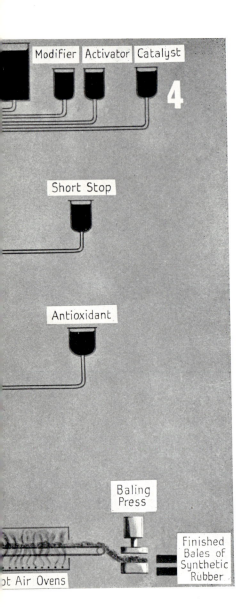

Modifier Activator Catalyst

4

Short Stop

Antioxidant

Baling
Press

Finished
Bales of
Synthetic
Rubber

ot Air Ovens

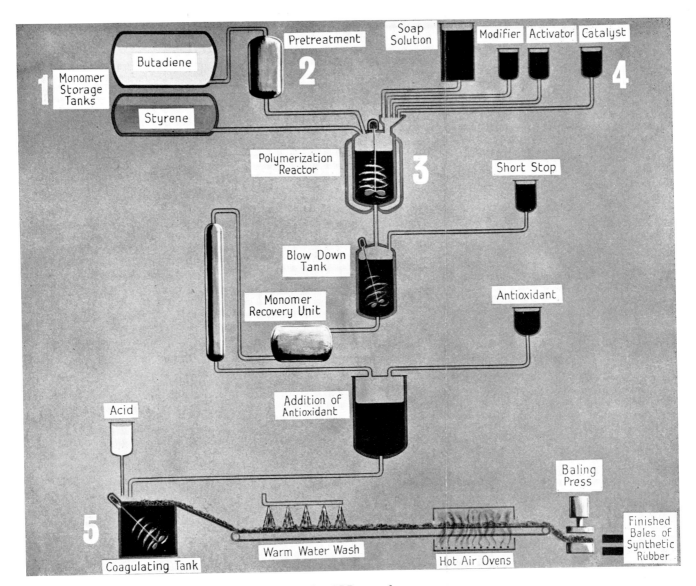

Fig. 8.   SBR manufacture.

bromo-butyl and chloro-butyl respectively, improves the vulcanising properties and permits admixture with natural rubber where this is desirable.

We have already mentioned that the low permeability of butyl to the passage of gases made it an automatic choice for the manufacture of inner tubes when natural rubber was in short supply during World War II. The advent of the tubeless tyre stimulated its use in other end

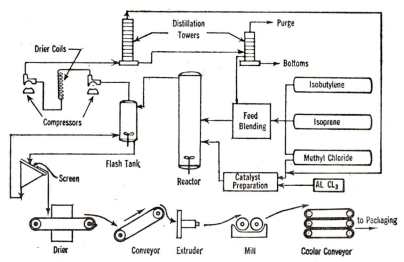

FIG. 9.   Flow sheet of Butyl manufacture.

products, where its good resistance to ozone and to high temperatures were the properties exploited. Butyl is now used in many 'mechanicals', in the curing bags and bladders used for tyre vulcanisation, and there has recently been marketed in the U.S.A. an all-butyl car tyre which is claimed to be much superior to existing tyres in riding comfort and cornering noise.

Nitrile Rubber

This is a co-polymer of acrylonitrile and butadiene, the method of manufacture being very similar to that used for the production of SBR. It is still occasionally referred to under its original trade names of Perbunan and Hycar OR, the 'OR' indicating 'oil resisting' — the outstanding property of this type of polymer. The degree of oil resistance depends on the proportion of acrylonitrile — the higher the acrylonitrile content the greater the oil resistance. However, flexibility at low temperatures becomes less as the amount of acrylonitrile increases and a balance must be struck. To give the compounder a reasonable choice the manufacturers supply nitrile rubbers with low, medium and high acrylonitrile contents, the range being from about 20% to 45%.

Processing is similar to natural rubber, but due allowance must be made for the toughness of the polymer. If the polymerisation is carried out at 41° F, as for cold SBR, an improvement in processing qualities is claimed. Scorch rate depends to some extent on the ancillary materials used in manufacture, one type of 'short stop' belonging to the thiocarbamate group of organic substances which we will meet later in their role of ultra accelerators for natural rubber.

Processing is improved by the use of 'ester' type plasticisers e.g. tricresyl phosphate (TCP) and dioctyl phthalate (DOP). The curing system is similar to that used for SBR, i.e. increased accelerator and reduced sulphur, compared to the proportions used in natural rubber compounding.

The end products made from nitrile rubber are those continuously exposed to oils and solvents; aircraft fuel tanks and a wide variety of hoses, oil seals and gaskets being typical applications.

Silicone Rubbers

Silicones are chemically 'compounds containing silicon, oxygen and organic groups'. The backbone of the polymer chain is composed of the silicon and oxygen atoms, combined as siloxanes, to which the organic groups are attached. Silicones may exist as either liquids or solids. Our main interest here is the solid elastomer but silicone oils in the form of emulsions are used in the rubber industry as release agents in moulding. Spraying the emulsion on the mould produces a silicone film which facilitates release of the product and gives it a good surface finish.

The method of manufacture of silicone rubber requires a series of complicated reactions much beyond the scope of this text and no description will therefore be attempted.

An interesting point regarding the long-term supply of elastomers may be mentioned at this stage. The only form of energy (in its scientific sense) required for the production of natural rubber is sunlight, but most synthetic rubbers make use of our large, but limited, supplies of stored sunlight in the form of coal and oil. Silicone rubber is one exception to this and it is comforting to know that the available amount of the element silicon is surprisingly large. It is found in the combined form in granites, sand-stones, rocks and clays, the earth's crust as a whole containing about 27% silicon.

Silicone rubber was first marketed about fifteen years ago; in those days it was very slow curing, it had very poor tensile strength, with only its resistance to high temperatures to recommend it. Self-curing formulations are now available and the use of silica fillers has greatly improved the physical properties. Although the ultimate tensile strength does not compare favourably with that of other elastomers, silicone rubbers retain their strength at temperatures far beyond those at which other rubbers would disintegrate — the working range extending from about — 135° F to 600° F. These superior properties must be paid for — silicone rubber costs about 30s. per lb. compared with around 2s. for SBR and butyl, and 2s. 6d. for natural rubber (at the time of writing).

Compounding of silicone rubbers is fairly simple, a three part mix of silicone gum, curing agent (usually benzoyl peroxide) and filler sufficing for most purposes. Processing is done on conventional rubber machinery, but requires care since the raw polymer is easily distorted. It should be borne in mind that any textile to be used with silicone rubber must also be capable of withstanding high temperatures — asbestos and glass fibre meet most requirements.

Polysulphide Rubbers

The polysulphide rubbers (trade name — Thiokol) were commercially available as early as 1932. Although they have outstanding resistance to the action of most organic solvents they have never attained bulk production. There are two main reasons for this — the tensile strength of the vulcanisate is rather low, and polysulphide rubbers have an obnoxious smell, particularly noticeable during mixing, but persisting even after cure.

Other Special-purpose Elastomers

Except to those students working in laboratories where new elastomers are evaluated, the following polymers will be names only. They are not in volume production, they are very expensive, but are listed to indicate the developments likely in the next few years in providing elastomers capable of meeting working conditions of ever-increasing severity.

Hypalon is the trade name of the Du Pont Co. Ltd. for polymers

C.R.T.

based on chlorosulphonated polyethylene. Three varieties are marketed, Hypalon 20, 30 and 40 all of which have outstanding resistance to weathering, ozone, chemicals and heat. They may be used in blends with other elastomers to improve the end products.

The name polyurethane is probably best known to the layman in the phrase 'polyurethane foam', a product which is challenging latex foam made from natural rubber latex. The solid rubbers based on polyurethanes — Vulcaprene, Adiprene and Genthane S are a few of the trade names — all show good resistance to oils, ozone and dry heat and thus deserve mention as special-purpose elastomers.

The treatment of butyl rubber with the chemical elements chlorine and bromine has already been noted. Fluorine is an element belonging to the same chemical family as chlorine and bromine — the 'halogen' family — and there are quite a number of fluorinated polymers in the special-purpose class. PTFE is the commonly accepted abbreviation for polytetrafluoroethylene, an elastomer with extremely good resistance to attack by chemicals. PTFE has a secondary role in the rubber industry, that of a release agent in intricate mouldings; the PTFE is sprayed on the mould to a thickness of about 0·0005 in. and, although expensive, the technique may be justified where a high degree of moulding accuracy is required. Teflon and Fluon are two well-known trade names for PTFE. Three other fluorinated rubbers are known by the trade names of Poly FBA, Viton A and Kel F.

Newer Elastomers

Stereo-chemistry is the study of the way in which the atoms in a molecule are arranged in space, i.e. as a three-dimensional structure. Stereo-regular (or stereo-specific) polymers are those in which the orientation of the molecule is controlled during the polymerisation reaction. In a way which we do not yet fully understand nature can exert such control when natural rubber and gutta percha are made. Both of these are based on a large number of repetitions of the C_5H_8 unit, but are put together in different ways, known to the chemist as cis 1, 4 and trans 1, 4 respectively. As we have seen, many elastomers have been synthesised, but it is only within the last few years that stereo-regularity in such syntheses has been achieved. This has been made possible by the work of K. Ziegler and G. Natta in developing catalysts which can direct the orientation of the molecule. Cis-polyisoprene (trade names — Isoprene Rubber, Natsyn, Ameripol

SN), cis-polybutadiene (Diene, Budene, Cis-4) and trans-polybutadiene are all now in commercial production and are being evaluated to determine where they may best be used in the manufacture of rubber products.

Another elastomer first commercially available in 1959 is ethylene-propylene rubber (EP rubber). Its impact on elastomer usage may be considerable in the near future, since the monomers are quite cheap and the conversion costs low.

High Styrene Resins

In the manufacture of SB rubber, the styrene and butadiene are used in the proportions of 25 : 75 respectively. If we reverse these proportions approximately the product is more of a resin than a rubber. Such high styrene resins in fine powder form are readily miscible with natural rubber or SBR and are widely used in shoe solings of various types. Butakon and Tred are two trade names for such resins.

Rubber Derivatives

In attempting to determine the chemical make-up of a substance it is customary to react with it other highly active chemicals, study the structure of the resulting products and thereby gain an insight into the manner in which the individual atoms are united in the original substance. In the study of natural rubber many derivatives were produced, only a few of which have attained commercial importance.

Treatment of rubber with certain chemicals changes the molecular structure from the normal long-chain form to ring-like structures. Such 'cyclised rubber' is a good reinforcing resin for natural rubber and has been used mainly in shoe soling materials. The modern method of manufacture is to add concentrated sulphuric acid to suitably-stabilised 60% centrifuged latex, hold the mixture at a temperature of approximately 212° F for about two hours, cool to 120° F and then add an equal amount of uncyclised latex. After coagulation, sheeting, washing to remove excess acid, and finally drying, the 50 : 50 masterbatch is ready for the market.

The reaction between rubber and hydrochloric acid produces rubber hydrochloride which finds its main use as a packaging film — trade name, Pliofilm.

Chlorinated rubber is produced by the action of chlorine on rubber. Its main commercial applications result from its chemical inertness — paints and coatings to protect surfaces against chemical attack. Chlorinated rubber is also used in bonding rubber to metal. The controlled reaction of oxygen on rubber results in oxidation products known as Rubbones used as additives to paints.

Prolonged mastication of natural rubber assisted by peptising agents degrades or 'depolymerises' the material until a liquid rubber is obtained. Vulcanisable fluid rubber compositions may then be produced by the addition of the usual fillers, oils, vulcanising ingredients, etc. One use of such composition is in inking rollers for the printing trade, the rubber roller being much superior to the orthodox gelatine composition roller.

As a result of research on improving natural rubber, there has been developed a series of raw materials made by either chemical combination or intimate mixture of natural Hevea rubber and other polymers. These have been given the generic term 'Heveaplus' and such 'graft polymers' of rubber and polymethylmethacrylate ('Perspex') and of rubber and polystyrene are now on the market. Such polymers have a combination of properties — high strength, high impact resistance and exceptional flex-cracking — not found in any other polymeric substance. Although the industrial importance of graft polymers is at present small, the development of such techniques is an interesting example of high polymer technology.

REFERENCES

READ, JOHN, *A Direct Entry to Organic Chemistry*. London.
COUZENS, E. G. and YARSLEY, V. E., *Plastics in the Service of Man*. Penguin Books.
STERN, H. J., *Rubber: Natural and Synthetic*. London.
Vanderbilt Rubber Handbook. 1958, New York, U.S.A.
FRANKLAND, P. G., An Ideal Rubber. *Proc. Inst. Rubber Ind.* 1958, Vol. 5, 186.
BOWDEN, W. and WILSON, A. J., Natural and Synthetic Polymers in Conveyor Belting. *Proc. Inst. Rubber Ind.* 1958, Vol. 5, 129.
BURRIDGE, K. G., Commercial Production of GR-S. *Proc. Inst. Rubber Ind.* 1957, Vol. 4, 178.
RUFFELL, J. F. E., Hypalon and Neoprene — Some Outstanding Properties. *Proc. Inst. Rubber Ind.* 1957, Vol. 4, 76.
ADAMS, R. J. and BUCKLER, E. J., Evolution and Application of Butyl. *Trans Inst. Rubber Ind.* 1953, Vol. 29, 17.
BUCKLER, E. J., and HARRIS, I. W. E., Butadiene-Acrylonitrile Co-polymers — Design, Synthesis and Use. *Trans. Inst. Rubber Ind.* 1955, Vol. 31 2.

BOLAM, S. E., Some Aspects of Nitrile Rubber Technology. *Rubber Journal and International Plastics*. 1957, Vol. 134, 924–7, 964–8, 1004–9

NOAD, R. B., Silicone Rubbers. *Proc. Inst. Rubber Ind.* 1954, Vol. 1, 116.

BLOOMFIELD, G. F. and STOKES, S. C., Cyclised Rubber, *Trans. Inst. Rubber Ind.* 1956, Vol. 32, 172

SPEIGHT, C., Liquid Rubber. *Rubber Developments*. 1955, Vol. 8, 18

BRPRA, Recent Developments in Heveaplus. *Rubber Developments*. 1956, Vol. 9, 2.

CHAPTER V

AN INTRODUCTION TO COMPOUNDING

The Necessity for Compounding

With one or two exceptions — crepe soles for footwear, pressure sensitive tapes — raw rubber is of little commercial value, and we will now consider the methods whereby it is modified by mixing with it a variety of substances, so chosen as to produce vulcanised rubber products with a wide range of properties from the toughest of tyre treads to the lightest of sponges. These substances are termed, in general, compounding ingredients, and most are not used solely in the rubber industry. Many of them, such as sulphur, zinc oxide, whiting, china clay, red iron oxide, etc., are met with in our daily lives and in other branches of industry, although special grades of these materials are often prepared for use in rubber.

The art of rubber compounding is often likened to that of the baker or pastry-cook, who takes flour as his raw material, adds to it definite quantities of other ingredients, blends them to a certain consistency, bakes the mixture for the required time and produces a heavy plum pudding or, with different ingredients of course, the lightest of puff pastry. Indeed, the cookery term 'recipe' is often used by rubber technologists when referring to the formula which gives the kinds and amounts of the materials comprising a rubber mix.

Compounding may be defined as the development of rubber mixes which will effectively withstand the conditions under which the products made from them are to be used; at the same time, the mixes so developed must be capable of being processed without undue difficulty in the factory. In a more limited sense, the term 'compounding' is applied to the assembly of the rubber and compounding ingredients in batch form ready for the mixing process proper. The product obtained when rubber and compounding ingredients are mixed together, ready for vulcanisation, is usually described by technologists as a 'compound'. Here we have one of the difficulties of rubber terminology, since chemically speaking it is not a compound,

38

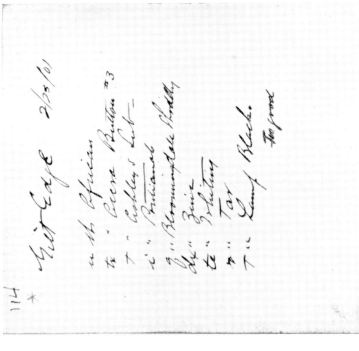

Fig. 10. Page from 'a little black book'.

but merely a mixture. On the shop floor, indeed, it is often called a mixing or mix. Stock, blend, quality or simply gum, are other commonly used terms for a rubber compound.

You might well ask why we must so modify our raw material following its production and I should like to quote what Dr. J. R. Scott, Scientific Adviser to the Rubber and Plastics Research Association of Great Britain has to say on the subject. "The object of rubber manufacture is to produce useful articles like tyres, hose, footwear and proofed garments from a raw material initially obtained in the form of latex. In the present state of our knowledge it is necessary to mix the rubber with an array of compounding ingredients, mostly powders. Yet the first step, so far as the bulk of rubber is concerned is to convert the fine fluid dispersion called latex into an intractable solid, into which, as it stands, it is impossible to mix anything. So the rubber has to be masticated or plasticised by drastic treatments necessitating massive and costly machinery and consuming millions of kilowatt-hours of valuable power, all of which is lost, most, indeed, 'going down the drain' in cooling water, or lost by heat radiation in present day 'hot' mastication.

Having thus got the rubber into a more tractable form (which in fact only means that we have severed the long-chain molecules into shorter ones) we proceed to mix into it an extraordinary variety of materials. Merely to effect the molecular cross-linking called vulcanisation we add sulphur, then one or more accelerators to speed up its action, then zinc oxide to boost the accelerator, then stearic acid to activate the zinc oxide; having done all this, the mix may turn out to be too lively, so we add a 'retarder' to tame the accelerator. Then in go all kinds of fillers or reinforcing agents, depending on whether the aim is merely to cheapen the mix, to give it stiffness, or to achieve the toughest and most wear-resisting product possible. The amount of these dry powders added may be so great that the mixture becomes unworkable, necessitating further additions in the form of softeners. Even now, success is not assured, for the completed mix must be heated under just the right conditions if the finished product is to have the desired properties. From our detached and impartial viewpoint, it is difficult to believe that these complex procedures and formulations represent the simplest and most scientific way of converting a long-chain polymer into a vulcanisate with the desired characteristics of stiffness, strength, resistance to tear and abrasion, and so on."

At this stage you will not comprehend fully all the points made by

Dr. Scott, but it is convenient to keep the quotation as a whole so that it may be referred to later on. You will note that in this rather gloomy picture, Dr. Scott, speaking in 1951, is careful to say that it represents rubber manufacture "in the present state of our knowledge". It is of course the present state of our knowledge with which we are concerned, but it should be said that development work now in progress indicates that, although the past hundred years have shown very considerable advances, rubber compounding will, in the not too distant future become even more of a science and less of an art.

In 1820, following Hancock's invention of his 'pickle' or internal mixer, as we would now call it, many different powders were mixed with rubber with the object of overcoming its tackiness and improving its durability, but it was not until Charles Goodyear's discovery of vulcanisation in 1839 that worthwhile developments were possible. As late as 1905, however, rubber compounding was very much a rule of thumb business and an astonishing variety of materials was added to rubber for no other reason than that they blended easily and could be added in large quantities without destroying completely the rubberiness of the product. Since rubber was an expensive and scarce commodity in those days, the primary object of such additions was to make it go further and thus cheapen the product. At that time rubber factories had no technical staff, the works foreman or factory manager being the only technical authority. A little notebook, the contents of which were closely guarded, held all his 'recipes' and process information; testing equipment was limited to his teeth, his fingers, a penknife and a blunt pencil point, and in a rough and ready fashion he could thereby determine strength, stretch, hardness and degree of vulcanisation. There were however no speedy and accurate methods for judging the effect of varying the kinds and amounts of compounding ingredients, and mix formulas were very unwieldy and hopelessly unscientific.

At the present time, when the technical assistant studying rubber compounding has access to a great volume of literature, which freely discusses the composition and methods of using the entire range of compounding ingredients, it is difficult to visualise the secrecy regarding rubber manufacture which existed in those early days. C. C. Davis, an eminent American rubber technologist, once said that he was expected to learn compounding without being permitted to know the mix formulas in use in his factory.

Some manufacturers, in order to keep secret the materials they used, would go so far as to buy them in small quantities from a large number of sources and, to add to the confusion, they were generally given fantastic names which bore no relationship to their compositions. As we shall see, some modern compounding ingredients have what would seem somewhat fantastic names, but these indicate the

" *Don't forget, Ernie boy—the merest soupcon of cyclohexyl benzthiazyl sulphenamide.*"

FIG. 11.

chemical composition of the material and fortunately are usually described by a generally accepted abbreviation or a short trade name.

One of the first studies of the effect of compounding ingredients on the physical properties of rubber was made in 1891 by two German chemists, Heinzerling and Pahl, and it was in the course of a similar investigation that S. C. Mote of the India Rubber and Gutta Percha Works at Silvertown, England, discovered in 1904 the beneficial effect of the addition of carbon black to rubber. The use of carbon black did not become general until several years later, for the motoring public took quite a bit of persuading to accept black tyres in place of the lighter-coloured ones to which they had been accustomed. The light colour resulted from the inclusion in the mix of zinc oxide, the best reinforcing ingredient known at that time. From 1910 onwards rule of thumb methods of compounding were gradually superseded by a more scientific approach which showed the technologist how to modify the properties of his mixtures on the basis of tests made on laboratory-mixed batches. Following a small-scale trial in the factory and, if necessary, the making of slight modifications to suit the particular processing equipment and methods, the final formulation is adopted for production.

The Development of Compounding

One aspect of the development of compounding is shown in Fig. 12 which displays in the form of a graph, the tensile strengths attained by various rubber compounds, after vulcanisation for different periods of time. The date alongside each curve indicates approximately when the compound was first used in manufacture. This study will serve as an introduction to the functions of some compounding ingredients, all of which will be dealt with in detail in Chapters IX and X.

Unvulcanised rubber has low strength (approximately 250 lbs. per square inch), it is sensitive to changes in temperature, it perishes quite rapidly and is swelled or dissolved by many liquids. Curve 1 represents a mixture of rubber and sulphur only, and it is seen that a considerable increase in strength has resulted. The compound is still too soft for most uses and the six hours vulcanising time

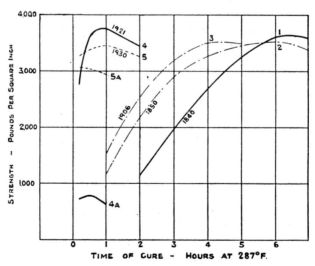

FIG. 12. Development of compounding.

is much too long to be commercially acceptable. The addition of a small quantity of zinc oxide was found to reduce slightly the time of cure necessary to develop maximum strength. From now on, we may use the shorter terms 'cure' and 'curing' when referring to vulcanising. The further time reduction seen in Curve 3 results from the addition of an accelerator to the rubber/sulphur/zinc oxide compound. The property that is speeded up by the use of an accelerator is the rate of cure, i.e. it accelerates the chemical reaction between the rubber and sulphur, and thus the compound develops its maximum strength either in a shorter time or at a lower temperature of cure, or both. Accelerators have other beneficial effects in rubber compounding but these do not concern us at the moment. The accelerator used in the compound corresponding to Curve 3 is aniline, a coal-tar product. This material, discarded shortly afterwards because of its poisonous nature, has been chosen here because it is the forerunner of most present-day accelerators, which are almost without exception, organic substances.

We will now be making frequent mention of organic and inorganic materials and a short explanation is necessary. In the course of the eighteenth century, those substances that are found in association with living organisms, either plants or animals, came to be termed 'organic'; those substances that are found in, or may be prepared from lifeless mineral matter were called 'inorganic' (not organic). It was later found that many of the so-called organic substances could be made in the laboratory without the intervention of any living organism, and they were all found to contain carbon as one of the constituent elements. Organic chemistry is nowadays simply defined as the chemistry of carbon and its compounds, while inorganic chemistry deals with all other substances.

Development of organic accelerators was quite rapid from 1906 onwards and Curve 4 shows the strength attained by a mix containing mercaptobenzothiazole, popularly abbreviated to MBT. The maximum strength is reached after only forty-five minutes curing time, which represents a tremendous advance. In evaluating perishing ('ageing' is the more scientific term) technologists cannot wait until the natural deteriorating influence of ozone, oxygen, heat, etc., has taken effect and several tests have been devised to compress into a few days a service life of several years. The mix represented by Curve 5 has been specially compounded to resist ageing, by the addition of an ingredient termed an antioxidant, also an organic chemical. The strength remaining after subjecting this mix to one of these 'accelerated ageing' tests is shown in Curve 5A. Compounds 1, 2 and 3 retain no strength at all after such a test and Compound 4 would not be considered sufficiently resistant to ageing, since it has lost about 80% of its original strength.

Requirements of the Customer

Rubber manufacturing companies are in business to make products which must satisfy the varied requirements of their customers, who may range from such large bodies as the Ministry of Supply and British Railways right down to the individual shopper. Large purchasers of rubber products often have testing facilities to ensure that the articles they buy are up to standard. The individual purchaser obviously cannot go to such lengths, but may have some degree of protection in the various consumers' associations existing in the United States and in the United Kingdom and now being set up in many other countries.

The job of the compound designer cannot stop, however, when he has satisfied the stringent customers' requirements. As has already been mentioned, the compounder uses small-scale machinery in a laboratory for his first tests, and it would be the height of folly to approve a compound for full-scale factory production solely on the basis of these results. Just as important as the customers' requirements are the processing requirements, since every compound must be capable of being handled on the existing factory machinery with a minimum of scrap and defective material. The consideration of what processing demands of a compound will be dealt with in Chapter VII after 'Processing Methods' have been described in the next chapter.

The maximum life of the product under the conditions of use is naturally of first importance to the customer. This calls for a rubber with good resistance to what is usually called 'ageing and weathering' and resistance to any other particular harmful influences the article may meet with, e.g. oxygen, ozone, sunlight, oils, acids or excessive heat. The required resistance to rubbing away — the abrasion resistance — may vary from that necessary to give maximum mileage from a tyre tread to the very low degree of abrasion resistance found in an eraser which must wear itself away rather than the paper. Maximum resistance to tearing is demanded of a tyre inner tube if punctures are not to extend, while some rubbers for wire covering must have a tear resistance low enough to facilitate easy stripping when jointing is to be done. Again the stretchability and snappiness of an elastic band would hardly be suitable in rubber flooring. Many rubber products are demanded in bright colours and most are required to have an attractive surface finish. Last, but most decidedly not least, the compounder must meet all the requirements at a cost which will enable the product to be marketed at a competitive price.

Here is an outline of some of the commonest physical tests used by the compounder in designing rubber mixes.

Strength

Materials may be subjected to a variety of deforming forces — extension, compression and that force akin to the closing of a pair of scissors, shearing. The loads which the material will withstand at the point of failure under these three types of deformation depend respectively on tensile strength, compression strength and shear strength. Here we are concerned only with the first of these, often quoted as just 'tensile', a less grammatical, but more familiar term, especially to older technologists. The strength of a particular rubber when stretched to its breaking point is not of itself of first importance, since few rubber articles are used anywhere near this limit. The property is often specified by the customer since it gives a good idea of the quality of the compound. It is used, along with other properties, in the laboratory evaluation of rate of cure. Tensile strength is expressed as the load required to break unit cross-section of the rubber — pounds per square inch (p.s.i.) in British units or kilograms per square centimetre (kg. per sq. cm.) in the metric system. Depending on the compound formulation, tensile strength at break may vary from as low as 500 p.s.i. to over 4,000 p.s.i.

Elongation

This is the name given to the amount of stretch or increase in length produced by applying a load to a test sample of rubber or to a rubber article. Again, few products are used at anywhere near the limit of stretch but the 'elongation at break' (or 'ultimate elongation') is often called for in specifications. It is stated as a percentage, i.e. if a marked section of a test strip originally 1 in. in length is 6 in. long at breaking point the elongation is 500%. The ultimate elongation of a tiling mix may be as low as 60%, and an inner tube compound may stretch over 700% before breaking.

Modulus

The term 'modulus' is derived from a Latin word meaning 'to regulate'. In rubber technology it is applied to the load required to stretch a rubber to a stated elongation. It is expressed in the same units as for tensile strength, pounds per square inch or kilograms per

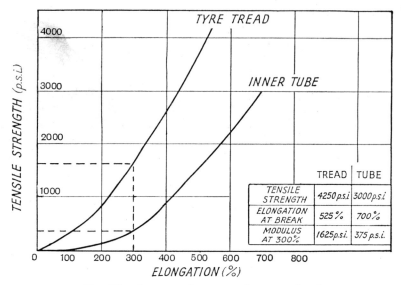

FIG. 13.   Stress-strain curves of tyre tread and
inner tube compounds.

square centimetre, and the elongation must be stated, otherwise the expression is meaningless.

The modulus of a rubber is a measure of its stiffness, the significance of which may be grasped if you consider the difference in effort required to stretch by hand, say, a rubber jar ring and a vacuum cleaner driving belt of similar diameter. Measurement of modulus is often used in routine testing of mixed compounds, a vulcanised ring of which is stretched over rollers on a simple form of tensile strength tester. At a pre-set elongation, the machine stops and a dial indicates the load which has been applied. If this is within the limits for the compound in question, the batch is passed as satisfactory for the next processing operation.

Fig. 13 shows in graphical form the relationship between the load applied to a test piece and the elongation produced by that load for two typical rubber compounds. These load/elongation, or stress/ strain, curves are characteristic of the compounds and of their state of cure. The big difference in the loads required to stretch the samples to 300% elongation, i.e. the modulus readings at 300%, should be particularly noted. The tyre tread stock is a 'high modulus' compound, the inner tube stock is a 'low modulus' compound.

Hardness

This property of vulcanised rubber is comparatively easy to measure since it does not involve destruction of the article and does not ordinarily require elaborate apparatus. It is often quoted in customers' specifications and has probably caused more argument between manufacturer and user than any other property of rubber. The hardness of vulcanised rubber may be defined as the resistance to penetration, without puncturing, of a blunt point impressed on the rubber surface. Within the last few years an International Scale of Hardness Degrees has been accepted, but it will be many years before this supersedes the wide variety of scales now in use. In quoting hardness figures it is therefore essential to state the instrument which has been used, e.g. 45° Shore A, 60° Short & Mason Rubbermeter, 75° Dunlop No. 3, etc. The most commonly used scales range from infinitely soft at 0° to rock hard at 100°. A tolerance should be agreed on, between manufacturer and customer, since a variation of a few points either way will not normally affect the performance of the article.

Some of the other properties which the designer must take into account when developing compounds, such as resilience and heat build-up, resistance to abrasion, to tear and to ageing, will be dealt with in Chapter XIII under 'Testing'. Colour and cost will be discussed with 'Compounding Ingredients'.

CHAPTER VI

PROCESSING MACHINERY AND METHODS

Now that we have discussed the reasons for modifying rubber by the addition of compounding ingredients, in short the 'why' of rubber compounding, we next consider 'how' this is done, that is, the methods and machinery employed in plasticising the rubber and preparing the unvulcanised mix. Then follows a short description of the various means by which this mix is shaped to produce an all-rubber article, such as rubber flooring, or combined with a textile material, as in the manufacture of waterproof clothing. In products such as tyres, belting and hose, the component parts, made by a variety of shaping methods, are finally assembled in the uncured state ready for the process of vulcanisation, which is the subject of Chapter VIII.

In discussing machinery for the processing of rubber, it must be borne in mind that the adoption of mechanisation and the size of the individual machines must be related economically, not only to the total volume of production, but also to the break-down of this total into the variety of products made, and, of equal importance, the range of sizes of any one product. No matter how reputedly efficient a machine might be, it would not be operating economically if it turned out a week's supply of a particular component in a few hours, and lay idle for the rest of the week; again the time spent in changing machine settings to suit size variations must be reasonably related to actual production time. These are some of the reasons for the great diversity in size and capacity of rubber processing machinery. In a tyre factory a comparison of the size of the tyre suitable for a small trolley with that for a large earthmoving vehicle lends point to this, and we can sympathise with Henry Ford when he said that customers could have a car in any colour so long as it was black.

This plant and equipment question is quite important since the advertisements in trade periodicals are apt to give the impression that the machinery depicted there, is in common use in the industry. However, it is only on rare occasions involving complete re-organisation that a modern layout can be adopted all at once, as in the new Russian tyre factory now being equipped by British machinery manufacturers. As early as 1941, an American firm published their plan for the 'Mill Room of the Future' stating that "this outline of the future mill room is imaginary only to the extent that such a mill room does not yet actually exist in entirety. But the individual production units do exist and are in use in the rubber and other industries, so that it remains only to gather all into one complete rubber processing plant". Generally units are purchased piecemeal, and technical and production staffs on the shop floor often have considerable difficulty in clearing the subsequent bottle-necks and maintaining an even flow of production.

It should also be remembered that if a piece of machinery or processing method has ever been described in the literature, no matter how long ago, it will quite probably be found in operation in some section of the industry. Such apparently obsolete methods should never be ridiculed by those trained in larger and perhaps more recently equipped factories, since the seemingly inefficient machine or process may fit in very well with the desired level of production, which may involve the transfer of labour from the manufacture of hot water bottles in summer to that of beach balls and bathing caps in winter.

If a new piece of plant, with which you are to be concerned either from a production or technical viewpoint, is being installed in the factory, it is useful to try and follow its erection and assembly, and later to check that the operating instructions so carefully compiled by the maker, are not lying idle in the files of the drawing office or buying department.

Mastication and Mixing

The preparation of the rubber mix comprises blending, mastication, compounding and mixing. Although we have noted previously that some degree of blending is carried out on the plantation, further blending of raw rubber from various consignments is advisable at the factory to help to smooth out the unavoidable variations in plasticity and rate of vulcanisation. Mastication aptly describes the operation of softening the rubber by milling so that the compounding ingredients may be added. Compounding, in its limited meaning, describes the assembly of the rubber and compounding ingredients in batch form ready for the mixing process proper, which blends the components to produce the finished unvulcanised mix. This is later formed into the

E   C.R.T.

required shapes and dimensions by the processes of calendering, extrusion and spreading.

It has already been pointed out that one of the disadvantages in the utilisation of raw rubber is its property of hardening at low temperatures. At the temperatures prevailing in the rubber producing countries, 85° F or thereabouts, rubber is quite soft and flexible, but if it is stored for any length of time at temperatures below 50° F it slowly hardens and may be received at the factory in a 'frozen' condition. Storage in a hot room at a temperature of about 140° F soon restores it to its original flexible state. Bales of 224 lb. weight must be split into pieces for easier handling, and blending is carried out by dispersing the cut pieces of single bales among different loads for mastication. When 70 lb. bales are used, a mastication load comprises several bales and blending is automatically ensured. Provided the splitting equipment is powerful enough, it is more economical to split the bale before thawing since the heat penetrates the cut pieces much more quickly than it does the complete bale. Bales have been torn down into separate sheets by hand or cut into slices on a power-driven saw, but the commonest method is to push the bale by hydraulic power against a knife with blades in the form of a star, thus producing six or eight pie-shaped sections.

Mastication may be done just prior to the mixing process proper, i.e. raw rubber is added to the mill or internal mixer and as soon as it is soft enough, the compounding ingredients are added. Mastication may also be done as a separate operation, the pre-masticated rubber being rested for some hours before passing to the mixing operation. Although there are machines which have been designed solely for mastication, most factories use either open roll mills or internal mixing machines for this process. The development of these latter machines may be conveniently discussed at this point.

Hancock's 'pickle' has already been mentioned in Chapter II. It consisted of a spiked roll operated by a crank handle working inside a spiked cylinder. This original machine, of only one man-power, produced about one pound of masticated rubber in three hours. It was soon superseded by larger machines of similar construction, except that iron was used instead of wood and the spikes were replaced by grooves. These machines, taking finally a load of about 200 lb. of rubber were the forerunners of the present-day internal mixers. The roller principle of masticating, mixing and sheeting rubber was first patented in 1836 by an American, Edwin M. Chaffee, his invention comprising a preparing machine (a two-roll mill) and a coating and covering machine (a four-roll calender). Apart from the continent of Europe the internal mixer did not find general acceptance until its design was radically improved in 1916, and mastication and mixing were until fairly recently carried out on mills based on Chaffee's invention.

The open roll mill (the term 'open' distinguishes it from the internal type of mixer) is a basic piece of rubber processing equipment. It is found in one form or another in all rubber factories, except those devoted solely to the manufacture of articles direct from latex — one of the advantages of latex processes is that heavy machinery such as mills and calenders is unnecessary. A mill consists of two hollow smooth-surfaced cast iron or steel rolls, set horizontally in bearings held in two end housings which are supported on a heavy base-plate. The rolls revolve towards each other, inwards at the top, and their distance apart, the 'nip', may be adjusted by screws set in the end housings. Shear discs ('safety caps') are located between the ends of these adjusting screws and the journal boxes in which the ends of the front roll are held. When a sudden excessive load is sustained by the mill, such as by the addition of frozen or very tough rubber, these safety discs fracture and save breakage of the rolls themselves. To prevent rubber and compounding ingredients running off the roll ends, and to keep lubricating oil and grease from getting back along the rolls into the batch, steel guides shaped to fit the roll contour very snugly are located at both ends. A mill pan is set below the rolls, its purpose being to catch any pieces of rubber which may fall from the batch or, when mixing is being done on the mill, to enable the compounding ingredients to be conveniently swept up for return to the nip. Production mills have rolls which vary in length from 30 in. to 84 in., roll diameters being respectively 14 in. and 28 in. Roll surface speeds may be as high as 100 ft. per min., the back roll generally travelling faster than the front. Opinions vary greatly as to what this difference should be, for the most efficient breakdown of the rubber structure or speedy blending of compounding ingredients, but the ratio $\dfrac{\text{back roll speed}}{\text{front roll speed}}$ which is termed the 'friction' ratio, may range from 1·1 : 1 to 1·4 : 1. If the speeds are the same, i.e. a friction ratio of 1·0 : 1, the rolls are said to be running at even speed. Cooling water is circulated through the rolls to give some degree of control of the rubber temperature.

These are the essential features of a two-roll rubber mill but there are a large number of variations on the basic construction. The back roll may be grooved, to give a better grip on the rubber entering the nip. In a washing mill or 'washer', both rolls are grooved and a spray of water may be played on the rubber as it passes through the nip. Washing mills were very necessary in the days when wild rubbers, containing impurities such as wood and sand, were in general use, and many washers had to be brought back into service during World War II when wild African rubber temporarily assumed considerable importance. A 'cracker' also has both rolls grooved, but this machine is of much heavier construction than an ordinary mill since its duty is to soften or plasticise, very speedily, slabs of rubber compound in preparation for extruding or calendering. Some masticating mills may be fitted overhead with a pair of slatted conveyors, an 'escalator', the purpose being to cool the rubber before it returns to the nip and so increase the efficiency of the mastication process. A refining mill has smooth rolls but has the same sturdy construction as a cracker. It runs at high speed, has a high friction ratio and its function is to break down any lumps or undispersed particles of compounding ingredients which might prove troublesome in subsequent processing. The incorporation of large amounts of powders into rubber on an open mill can be quite laborious. A short conveyor belt, called an 'apron', running below the rolls and brought up into contact with the rubber on the front roll, automatically returns the powders to the nip without the need for continual sweeping up. The apron may be dropped away from the front roll to permit the usual cutting and rolling of the rubber which disperses the compounding ingredients evenly throughout the batch. Mills used solely for warming up stock to be fed to an extruder or calender, may have a variety of auxiliary devices, for keeping the rubber active on the mill, and usually have a set of knives for cutting off a continuous strip of the warmed stock which is then transferred by conveyor to the extruder feed hopper or to the calender nip.

The internal mixer might be considered as a two-roll mill enclosed in a strong metal box. The principle is the same as that of the open mill — rubber being worked between metal surfaces — but the contours of the rotors and mixing chamber are so designed to ensure that shearing of the rubber will take place throughout the entire chamber. This accounts for much of the greater efficiency of an internal mixer compared to that of the open mill with its single nip. The rotors are cut in the form of an interrupted spiral and revolve at slightly different speeds. The clearance between the tips of the rotors and the walls of the casing depends on the size of the machine, being about $\frac{1}{2}$ in. for the popular No. 11 Banbury mixer. Incidentally, in some quarters it is common to use the term 'Banbury' as synonymous with 'internal mixer'; this should be avoided, since this particular make (originally designed in America by F. H. Banbury), is only one of several types of such machines. The bottom of the mixing chamber is a separate unit, wedge-shaped to improve the mixing action, and it acts as a sliding or drop door through which the batch is dumped. The rubber and other ingredients are added through a hopper on top of the machine where an air-operated ram, forming the upper surface of the 'box', exerts pressure on the batch and prevents it riding up the hopper. The rotors, casing, door and ram are all water-cooled and a thermometer pocket, usually coupled to a recording chart, is fitted in the mixing chamber to indicate the temperature of the batch. Since the completed batch is dumped in a number of large chunks, the internal mixer is usually mounted over an open mill on which the stock is sheeted, or the batch may be dumped on a short conveyor belt which transfers it to an adjacent mill. Internal mixers are made in a range of sizes from laboratory models up to those taking 600 lb. of raw rubber.

Mastication of rubber may be done on any of the two-roll mills described above (smooth rolls, grooved back roll, 'escalator' mill), in an internal mixer or in a machine, a 'Plasticator', designed solely for mastication. This is really a large extruding machine in which a screw (20 in. diameter in the largest size) forces the rubber along a barrel and effectively plasticises it.

Mastication on open mills is somewhat of a haphazard process — the rubber is loaded on the mill, cooling water usually turned on full, and the rubber cut and rolled, perhaps for a specified time or until the operative thinks it is soft enough. Variable results in the subsequent processing were regarded as inexplicable until it was realised that the temperature at which the rubber was masticated had a profound effect on its final plasticity. Plasticity in relation to rubber-like materials is a difficult term to explain. The word itself means 'mouldable' and was applied originally to potter's clay, which retains completely the shape given to it by the hands of the potter and shows no tendency to spring back or recover its undeformed shape. Prolonged mastication can produce a 'dead' or 'dead milled' rubber with little or no recovery but most masticated rubbers and rubber compounds exhibit some degree of both softness and recovery, which properties taken together determine their plasticity. The graph in Fig. 14 shows the effect on plasticity of varying the temperature of mastication. The exact meaning of 'Mooney viscosity' need not be given at present; it is sufficient to say that on this scale of plasticity a high number means a tough rubber, a

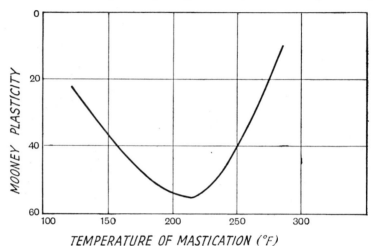

FIG. 14. Relationship between plasticity and mastication temperature.

low number means a soft one. The shape of the curve shows quite clearly that for most efficient mastication we should arrange conditions so as to avoid rubber temperatures of 190° F to 220° F; mastication is therefore now spoken of as 'cold', corresponding to the left-hand part of the curve and 'hot', which corresponds to the right-hand part. Due to the high temperature required (290° F to 300° F), hot mastication is normally carried out only in an internal mixer, which may dump the batch automatically when the specified temperature is attained. The efficiency of mastication is much increased by the addition to the rubber of small quantities of certain organic chemicals, termed 'peptisers', of which MBT, better known as an accelerator, is one example. Peptisers work best on hot mastication, but some types are effective at the lower temperatures attained on open mills.

Compounding

The precise set-up for the assembly of the rubber and compounding ingredients varies according to the size of the factory. For the

FIG. 15.   Rotors of internal mixer (K4 Intermix).

smaller user the grocer's shop equipment of a ham-knife, scoop and a set of weighing scales may suffice, while the larger manufacturer may employ a fully automatic weighing method which adds the specified quantities of the ingredients to a conveyor belt, which carries them to the mixing machine. This latter method requires that the materials be free-flowing and most manufacturers of compounding ingredients will supply in this form. The most up-to-date plants use rubber compounds also in pellet form, produced by a special fitment which extrudes the rubber in rod form and automatically cuts it into short lengths.

Calendering

Machines for calendering are found in several industries — paper is finished on a calender, laundries use another type as an ironer and the rapidly growing plastics industry uses calenders very similar to those used in our own industry. Chaffee's original machine was called the 'Mammoth' because of its dimensions. Improvements have been made and the inventor would have some difficulty in recognising the modern machine, not because the principle has changed but probably on account of the numerous devices added for easy, speedy operation and continuous production of rubber sheet or rubber-coated fabric of uniform thickness throughout its length and width.

Although some simple forms of calender have only one function (a 'doubling' machine is simply a large mangle used for sticking together two plies of rubbered fabric) most consist of three or four rolls and may be operated in a variety of ways. Incidentally, the rolls of a calender are still frequently referred to as 'bowls', this term being a relic of the days when all large rollers were wooden and made from the trunks or 'boles' of trees. A calender may be considered as a kind of precision mill (two-bowl machines used in the footwear industry are good examples of this) but every additional bowl forms another nip at which the rubber compound is conditioned, thus improving its uniformity when taken off in sheet form or coated on a textile material. The three-bowl type is the commonest for general use, while four bowls are employed in the largest tyre factories for coating both sides of tyre cord in one pass. This operation may also be done by running two three-bowl calenders in 'train', the fabric passing through each calender in turn; depending on production requirements the calenders may, of course, be used separately. It is impossible to include here all the possible variations in position of bowls, rubber feeding and batch-up methods, auxiliary rolls, etc., due to the extraordinary versatility of the calender. A large number of diagrams showing these features ('threading' diagrams) will be found in the references at the end of the chapter.

Many operating and engineering difficulties (roll adjustment, bowl deflection) result from having the bowls superimposed on one another. If the top bowl is positioned on a level with the second top in

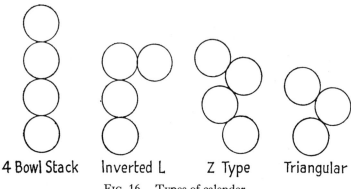

| 4 Bowl Stack | Inverted L | Z Type | Triangular |

FIG. 16.   Types of calender.

'breast' or 'inverted L' formation these difficulties are minimised, and further improvement is claimed for the modern 'Z' type, although it will be some considerable time before these are in common use. In line with the four-bowl 'Z' design, the three-bowl is now available in 'triangular' formation (see Fig. 16).

Calenders are made in a variety of sizes from laboratory models with rolls 12 in. long, 6 in. diameter up to production models with rolls 105 in. long by 32 in. diameter. Bowls are of chilled iron, bored for circulation of steam and water to give accurate control of temperature. Speed must be smoothly variable up to the maximum of which the machine is capable and means must be provided for changing the relative speeds of the bowls — in the 'frictioning' process on a three-bowl calender the bottom roll runs at about two-thirds of the speed of the middle roll to wipe or smear the rubber into the fabric. The production of rubber sheet or coated fabric of uniform dimensions both lengthwise and crosswise is a matter of considerable difficulty, but is very important both from the economic aspect and also from its effect on the later assembly of the product. Calender bowls will deflect slightly due to their weight and further deflection results from the action of loading them with rubber compound. Fig. 17 shows the commonest way of counteracting this and producing even thickness across the width of the material. The convexity of the top roll and concavity of the bottom roll may be only a few thousandths of an inch and, unfortunately, corrects the roll deflection for only a very limited range of compounds. An improved method, difficult to apply to existing calenders, however, is to fit special bearings which permit

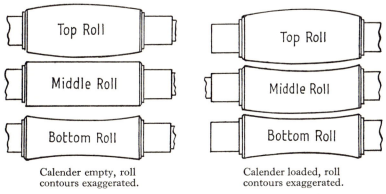

Calender empty, roll contours exaggerated.

Calender loaded, roll contours exaggerated.

FIG. 17.   Calender bowl deflection.

the axis of the top roll to be moved slightly in relation to that of the middle roll, giving the effect of opening the nip at the roll ends more than at the centre. A calender with this modification is termed a 'swivel-roll' or 'crossed-axes' machine. Uniformity of thickness along the length of a roll of sheet compound or of coated fabric demands that the calender nip be fed with a uniform supply of correctly warmed compound of the specified plasticity. Hand feeding by strips or 'dollies' of stock may be adequate for many purposes, but the ideal method is to feed the nip by a strip removed continuously from the warming mill and transferred to the calender by a narrow conveyor belt, the final section of which is oscillated back and forth across the nip, the so-called 'pendulum' feed. Calenders may be fitted with various instruments for indicating and controlling roll temperatures, for measuring and recording rubber thickness, etc., but the operation of calendering is still very much an art and a good calender operator, aided by a gang who know the meaning of team work, is an asset to any mill-room.

It will easily be seen that mills and calenders have many potential hazards which might result in operative injury. The question of safe operation will be discussed in Chapter XIV under 'Safety and Health'.

Extrusion

This is a manufacturing method of extreme importance in most branches of the rubber industry. The process consists in forcing warm unvulcanised stock through a die to give long lengths of rubber of a definite cross-section. Extruding or 'forcing' machines are used in the manufacture of tubing, hose, pneumatic tyre treads and inner tubes, solid tyres, stair treads and nosings, draught excluders, etc. A simple form of extruder, operated by a piston as in an icing set, was known about 1856 but it was not until the 1880's that we first hear of the well-known names of Shaw, Iddon and Royle. Development in those days was slow, since rubber factories were closed to outsiders and the firm of Royle was making extruders for more than twenty years without any member of the firm ever getting into a factory to see a machine in operation.

An extruder consists of four main parts: the barrel (or cylinder), the worm (or screw), the head (or die-box), and the drive. The drive, usually by variable speed motor, rotates the screw in the barrel and pushes warmed rubber stock (fed into a hopper on top of the screw) up to the front of the machine to which is fitted the die-box. The die is clamped in the die-box, and the extruded section issues therefrom on to a variable speed belt conveyor. The cylinder is jacketted and may thus be steam-heated or water-cooled. In modern machines the screw also is water-cooled. The size of an extruding machine is indicated by the screw diameter which varies from 1 in. in laboratory models to 12 in. for the largest production unit.

For solid sections the die is clamped in the head and little adjustment is necessary, but for tubing of any description the operation is more complicated. The outside circular shape is given by a die screwed into the head of the machine, while the hollow inner part is produced by a conical nozzle which is supported in the stream of rubber by being fixed to a core-bridge or 'spider', which is itself fixed in the head of the machine just in front of the screw. The wall thickness of the tubing is fixed by the relative movement of die and nozzle; in some machines the spider and nozzle are adjusted in relation to a fixed die, while others may vary the die setting in relation to a fixed nozzle. In the extrusion of pneumatic inner tubes, the die has a screw thread for fitting to the head, and an all-over variation in

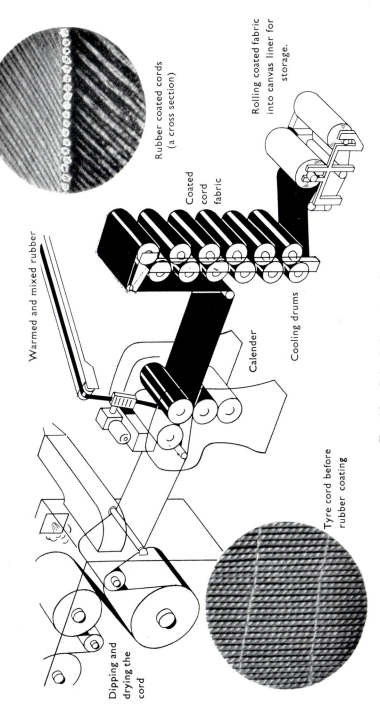

Rubber coated cords
(a cross section)

Coated cord fabric

Rolling coated fabric into canvas liner for storage.

Warmed and mixed rubber

Calender

Cooling drums

Dipping and drying the cord

Tyre cord before rubber coating

Fig. 18.   Calendering tyre cord.

wall thickness is obtained by screwing the die further into, or out of the head, thus changing the aperture formed between die and nozzle. The spider used in this operation is usually water-cooled. To prevent the hot sticky inner walls of the tube from adhering, once the tube has issued from the die and nozzle, a puff of air laden with soapstone is blown inside, via a hole in spider and nozzle. The set-up for the extrusion of inner tubes is shown in Fig. 19.

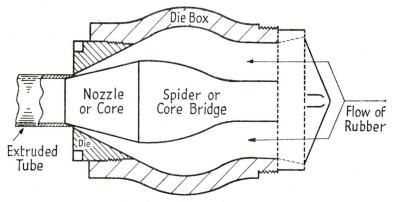

FIG. 19.   Extrusion of tubing.

The extruder has reached its greatest efficiency in tyre manufacture, over 70% of the rubber in a tyre being extruded. A typical set-up comprises a cracker and warming mills from which a strip feed passes to the feed box of the extruder. The tread issues on to a variable speed belt conveyor, where specified width is obtained, over a scale device to ensure correct weight, thence to two small calenders which apply the undertread and cushion rubbers, into a cooling tank and finally to a machine which cuts to specified length.

The design of dies for tubing is fairly simple, but for irregularly shaped solid sections the position is made difficult by the different speeds of the rubber at the various parts of the die. No hard and fast rules can be laid down, and design is a matter of trial and error. A thin tapered section may require spue holes at the edges to even up the rubber flow and give a smooth edge to the section.

In wire covering the head is usually T-shaped, the wire passing through the head at right angles to the line of the screw. In cable covering the nozzle is hollow to permit the cable to pass through and pick up its layer of rubber formed between die and nozzle tip.

By fitting a special head equipped with fine gauzes supported by a strong perforated plate, the extruder may be used for straining raw rubber or rubber compound to remove foreign matter of any kind. The modern 'strainer-slabber' illustrates another useful function of the extruder, production of a flat sheet by slitting a tube as it issues from the die. As in calendering, uniform dimensions of the extruded section demand a uniform supply of warmed compound of the correct plasticity, and again team work on the part of the extruder gang will facilitate subsequent processing.

The Barwell Batch Extruder is a novel type of extruder recently developed mainly for the production of tread rubber ('camelback'), the strip of, usually, trapezium section used in the retreading of pneumatic tyres. The slab rubber is warmed in a steam-heated oven, then rolled into a 'pig' or 'dolly' and fitted into the barrel of the extruder where a ram forces it out through the die.

Spreading

This is a method of applying a coating of rubber to a fabric, but differs from calendering in that it can apply much thinner coats ($\frac{1}{2}$ to $1\frac{1}{2}$ thousandths of an inch) and can handle very light fabrics which are difficult to calender successfully. Fabrics for the waterproof garment trade are prepared by spreading, the mix being made into a thick dough by treating it with a rubber solvent. In the ordinary meaning of spreading the knife moves over the material, in rubber spreading it is more convenient to move the fabric under a stationary blade at the back of which a 'bank' of dough is maintained. The spreading machine was invented by Thomas Hancock in 1837 and has changed very little since then, except that nowadays the solvent evaporating from the spread dough is trapped and recovered for further use.

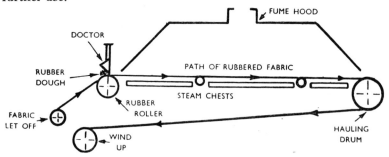

FIG. 20.   Diagram of roller spreading machine.

Dipping

This method of manufacture is used for thin articles such as bottle teats, surgeons' gloves and balloons. The rubber compound is dissolved in solvent to make a thin solution and formers of the required shape are immersed in it. They are withdrawn slowly, rotated to drive off the solvent and the process is repeated until a sufficient thickness of rubber has been built up. Vulcanisation is normally by the 'cold cure' method which will be discussed in Chapter VIII. The use of a concentrated latex is displacing rubber solution to a large extent in the manufacture of dipped goods.

REFERENCES

MORRIS, E., Rubber Processing Machinery: Development in Design. *Proc. Inst. Rubber Ind.* 1956, Vol. 3, 95

WAKE, W. C., Mill Room Productivity, Part I. *Trans. Inst. Rubber Ind.* 1957, Vol. 33, 71

DANIEL, T. J. and WAKE, W. C., Mill Room Productivity, Part II. *Trans. Inst. Rubber Ind.* 1957, Vol. 33, 135

DANIEL, T. J. and WAKE, W. C., Mill Room Productivity, Part III. *Trans. Inst. Rubber Ind.* 1958, Vol. 34, 79

SEAMEN, R. G. and MERRILL, A. M., *Machinery and Equipment for Rubber and Plastics.* New York, U.S.A.

WILLSHAW, H., *Calenders for Rubber Processing.* London

CHAPTER VII

PROCESSING REQUIREMENTS OF
RUBBER COMPOUNDS

Now that we have outlined what the customer requires of a rubber compound and discussed the processing methods by which this compound is prepared for manufacture, we must look at the relationship of the compound formula to the requirements of processing. In manufacturing end products to sell at a competitive price, it is the function of management to ensure that use is made of the minimum quantities of the most economical materials which will give both trouble-free processing and a product with a satisfactory service life. 'Economical' here does not mean 'cheapest' since first cost is definitely not the only standard of judging a raw material. A reasonable margin over the minimum service requirements will be allowed, of course, since the possibilities of accidental or deliberate misuse of the product will be known to the compound designer.

In formulating a mix for any particular use, the compounder nowadays does not need to start from scratch as was necessary in the old 'locked compound book' days. Most suppliers of raw materials to the rubber industry maintain excellently equipped laboratories from which issues a spate of information in the form of pamphlets, brochures and handbooks in which may be found basic mix formulas for practically every rubber product. Selection of a number of possible compounds is easy and the compounder can soon make a laboratory check to ensure that they will meet the customers' requirements; it would be unreasonable to expect the supplier to guarantee that the results he quotes would be obtained by every laboratory in view of the large number of variables involved. As has already been stressed, it is most unlikely that such a basic compound will meet the processing requirements of the particular factory and here the compounder must rely on past experience. In the early days of compound development, disillusionment often came to those who thought that a personal copy of one firm's compound formulas would act as the 'open sesame' to any other organisation in the same branch of the industry — they did not realise that suiting a compound to the equipment available is as important as knowing the basic formula. Most processing methods require the application of heat to the rubber compound, and it is not difficult to understand why a compound developed for use in Britain would not process satisfactorily in India. Even in countries having similar climates, differences in processing will be encountered between district and district, factory and factory. A hot summer may require a slight change in the formula of a compound which is perfectly satisfactory during the other three seasons. The reason for all this is simply that there are so many variables quite outwith the control of the compounder — different sources of raw materials and types of equipment, variation in air temperatures and humidity, and variation in amount and temperature of cooling water supplied to mills, calenders and extruders. The experience of the operatives must also be considered — one particular shift or gang will often report trouble not experienced by others carrying out the same process. If the compounder is not to be overwhelmed with demands for formula modifications, it is essential that those members of the technical staff whose duty it is to control the process must be able to make up their minds very quickly whether processing difficulties are real ones requiring attention, are real but will disappear with greater operative experience, or are purely imaginary. Rubber compounds are identified in the factory by codes consisting of numbers and/or letters, and many compounders will often have received a crop of complaints following a simple code number change (perhaps for reasons of rationalisation or avoidance of confusion) without any change in the compound formula. On the other hand, it is not advisable, to say the least, to make anything more than a very minor change in a compound without informing those responsible for its processing.

To ensure that equipment gives its maximum productivity high processing speeds and short times of vulcanisation are desirable. Short cure times necessitate fast-curing compounds while high processing speeds result in increased heat generation with the risk of the vulcanisation reaction starting prematurely. A balance must therefore be struck between these two opposing requirements — minimum curing time and processing safety. This premature starting of the vulcanisation reaction is one of the rubber industry's most serious problems; some years ago, an American estimate put the loss at the high figure of 3% to 5% of total sales. The widespread nature of the problem is illustrated very clearly by the extraordinary variety of names given to the effect — pre-curing, scorching, burning, firing up, curing up, setting up, bin curing, pile curing, etc. 'Scorching' is the most commonly used term although the others may be met with, in describing particular stages of processing at which the scorching has taken place.

For a proper understanding of the scorch problem it must be realised that the chemical reaction known as vulcanisation starts as soon as the curing ingredients have been added to the rubber. These curing ingredients (or curatives) are generally sulphur, accelerator and accelerator activators. The speed with which the reaction proceeds, assuming the same quantities and types of curatives, depends on two factors — the temperature to which the mix is heated and the time it is held at that temperature. To use a modern phrase, every working and reworking of the mix necessitated by the processing methods employed, adds to the 'heat history' of the mix, and pushes the reaction a little further along the scale from the uncured to the cured state. Technicians are interested mainly in how the effect shows itself, i.e. what happens to the rubber on the mill, calender or extruder, but it is instructive to know what is thought to happen to the molecular structure of the rubber when vulcanisation takes place.

In Chapter I we learned that a piece of uncured rubber consists of a very large number of coiled long-chain molecules which are considerably entangled but are not linked together in any way. If such a piece of rubber is stretched the change in dimensions arises in two ways, (a) the coiled-up molecules straighten themselves out, returning to their original state when the stretching force is removed, and (b) molecular chains slip over one another, a permanent effect which is not reversed when the stretching of the rubber is stopped. When the curatives are added and heat applied, the vulcanisation reaction starts, and it is believed that the sulphur forms bridges or cross-links between different molecules. If a piece of this cured rubber is now stretched, uncoiling of the molecules is still possible but the tendency for the molecules to slide over one another is very much reduced. The differences between cured and uncured rubber are already familiar to you — cured rubber has increased strength, increased resistance to ageing and to the action of oils and solvents, is less affected by changes in temperature — but another way of expressing the effect of vulcanisation is to say that we have suppressed the plasticity of the rubber and enhanced its elasticity. Plasticity is that property possessed by certain solid materials in keeping the shape given them by a deforming force; elasticity is the opposite of plasticity, it is that property possessed by solid materials which tend to return to their original shape after removal of a deforming force. The term 'elasticity' is also applied, somewhat unscientifically, to the large distance to which some vulcanised rubber may be stretched without losing the ability to

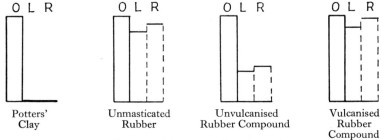

Potters'	Unmasticated	Unvulcanised	Vulcanised
Clay	Rubber	Rubber Compound	Rubber
			Compound

FIG. 21.   Plasticity testing by comparison.

O =original height, L =loaded height, and R =recovered height of pellet.

return very nearly to the original length. It is not difficult to see, therefore, that in uncured rubber it is the plasticity that predominates and in cured rubber elasticity predominates.

These ideas may be clarified if they are expressed in terms of how plasticity is measured. In one form of 'plastometer' (an instrument for determining the plasticity of rubber) a small sample in the shape of a cylinder 1 centimetre (cm.) high and 1 sq. cm. in area, is squeezed between two little plates (or platens) by loading the upper platen with a weight. After a specified time of compression, say thirty seconds, the thickness of the sample is measured, the weight on the upper platen is removed and the sample allowed to recover. The thickness is again measured after a further thirty seconds of recovery. The sample thickness after compression compared to the original thickness gives a measure of the plasticity of the rubber, while the thickness after removal of the weight compared to the compressed thickness gives a measure of its recovery. Fig. 21 shows, diagrammatically, such a test being carried out on (a) clay, (b), unmasticated rubber, (c) unvulcanised rubber compound, and (d) the same compound vulcanised. We find that the clay will spread out as thin as the platens will allow it. It is fully plastic and shows no recovery. The unmasticated rubber will compress slightly and recover quite considerably. As we have already seen, such raw rubber shows quite high elasticity, often referred to in

F   C.R.T.

this connection as 'nerve'. The uncured compound will deform and show recovery depending on the type of compound — tyre tread, belt friction, floor tile, etc. The cured sample of the same compound will deform very little under compression, and recovery will be almost complete since the vulcanisation reaction has destroyed its plasticity and increased its elasticity.

If we repeat this experiment with a number of samples all of the same compound but heated before testing for a range of times at, say, $250°$ F, it will be found that as the time of heating is increased, i.e. as the vulcanisation reaction proceeds, there is a steady reduction in plasticity and increase in recovery. This is one form of 'scorch test' and the number of minutes of heating for the compound to reach a certain recovery is an index of its processability.

Scorching is most likely to occur during mixing, during warming-up prior to processing or during the actual calendering or extrusion. The smooth surface of the mix begins to roughen and small particles of cured rubber, originally few in number, increase in size and number until the entire surface presents a 'burnt' appearance. Unless action is taken to remove the semi-cured material, the whole mass will crumble and fall from mill or calender rolls. This is the most striking manifestation of scorching and in one sense it is the simplest. The material is obviously useless for the purpose for which it was intended and there is no temptation to pass it on to the next stage. Regrets about the wasted material and the production lost due to the interruption of the process will come later; the immediate action should be to ascertain why the scorching took place. At the other end of the scale, a very slight degree of scorch or 'set up' may pass unnoticed right through all processing stages and its presence may be inferred only by the return of products which have split up, or delaminated, in service.

Table IV summarises the processing equipment and methods dealt with in Chapter VI and leads on to the methods of vulcanisation to be discussed in Chapter VIII. If we look at the 'Problems Involved' column and bear in mind the problem of scorching, it is obvious that, for the most efficient processing, rubber compounds should have

      (i) uniform plasticity and recovery.
     (ii) uniform scorch rate.
and (iii) uniform rate of cure.

(i) requires that batch after batch of compound must calender to the same dimensions with the same nip setting of the bowls, must extrude through a given die to the same dimensions and at the same speed. Most processing and assembly operations produce a quantity of uncured compound (trimmings, residue, uncured waste, raw scrap) which must be worked away with new compound. The plasticity limits should be set to allow for the addition of the expected quantity of this waste, which ideally should go right back for incorporation at the mixing stage, since it is difficult to get operatives to space out its addition during warming up.

(ii) requires that, taking into account the expected variations in volume and temperature of cooling water, in air temperature and in the working and reworking of the compound, no sign of any premature starting of the vulcanisation reaction shall be apparent.

(iii) requires again that with reasonable control of conditions, the state of cure of the end product shall be uniform, heater load after heater load, shift after shift. Control of conditions refers here to such details as times of loading and unloading heaters and moulds, since all the factors involved in the curing schedule itself, (time, temperature and pressure) should ideally be controlled automatically.

We should now understand more clearly the 'Problems Involved' column in Table IV. Under the headings given there, let us amplify our general discussion of processing requirements by indicating a few stages where trouble may be met.

Rubber Softening

The advisability of cutting a 'frozen' bale of 224 lb. before putting in the hot room for softening has already been stressed. The use of rubber which has not been completely unfrozen will give wide variations in plasticity and may lead to subsequent scorching.

Mastication

In Chapter VI the differences between 'cold' and 'hot' mastication were dealt with and the reason given for avoiding rubber mastication temperatures in the range 190° F to 220° F. In factories handling a variety of rubber products it may be necessary to carry three grades of pre-masticated rubber (i) lightly masticated for stiff stocks (ii) medium grade for calendering compounds and (iii) very highly masticated (or 'dead' masticated) for friction stocks, rubber solutions and sponge mixes. Since the use of one of these in place of another would completely upset processing, it is essential that the grades be clearly distinguished by suitable marking.

TABLE IV. PROBLEMS OF RUBBER PROCESSING

Operation	Equipment	Object	Problems involved
Rubber softening	Hot rooms	To 'unfreeze' and soften rubber	Time; temperature; low thermal conductivity of rubber
Bale splitting	Saw or 'star' cutter	Size reduction to suit mastication equipment	Removal of outer covering; foreign matter
Mastication	Open mill, internal mixer or 'Plasticator'	To plasticise rubber for incorporation of compounding ingredients	Time; temperature
Masterbatching	Open mill, internal mixer	To reduce equipment contamination; to ensure accuracy of weighing small amounts of comp. ingreds.; to improve dispersion	Time; temperature
Mixing	Open mill, internal mixer	To obtain a homogeneous mixture of rubber and compounding ingredients	Time; temperature; dispersion; scorch; cooling
Storage	Slabs or pallets, rolls in racks, pellets in hoppers or silos	To maintain a buffer stock to suit production requirements; to permit testing before use	Temperature before and during storage; time before re-use; bin or pile curing
Warming up	Cracker mill, open mill or internal mixer	To bring to temperature and plasticity required for next process	Time; temperature; mill loading; re-use of uncured trim or waste
Calendering: Sheeting	Calender	To provide sheet rubber for building product	Plasticity; recovery; roll temperature; scorch
Coating	Calender	To apply rubber to fabrics	Plasticity; recovery; roll temperature; scorch
Frictioning	Calender	To apply a tacky anchor coat to fabrics	Plasticity; recovery; roll temperature; scorch
Profiling	Calender	To produce sections of specified profile	Plasticity; recovery; roll temperature; scorch
Extrusion	Extruder	To produce long lengths of specified cross-section (solid or tubular); to cover wire, hose, etc.	Speed of machine; temperature; plasticity; recovery; scorch

Operation	Equipment	Object	Problems involved
Assembly	Specialised equipment depending on the product	To assemble tyres, hose, footwear, belting, etc., ready for curing	Shrinkage; tack; bloom; incipient set up
Vulcanisation	Hydraulic press and moulds	To obtain desired size and shape during cure	Lubrication; flow of compound; uniformity of cure
	'Open steam' autoclave	To obtain desired dimensions by curing in direct contact with steam, embedded in chalk or wrapped with cloth lining	Uniformity of temperature in autoclave; change of shape during cure; sagging; blistering; porosity
	Pressure heater using air or other gases	To cure without surface deterioration	Uniformity of temperature in autoclave; change of shape during cure; sagging; blistering; porosity
	Festoon heater	To cure coated fabrics	Uniformity of temperature
	'Cold cure' apparatus	To cure coated fabrics	Time; concentration of solution; sweetening

Masterbatching

A masterbatch or mother stock is a non-vulcanisable mix consisting of rubber and, generally, only one other ingredient, the proportion of which is much higher than will be present in the final production mix. Masterbatches are used for convenience and cleanliness (carbon black and colour masterbatches prevent contamination of mixing equipment with loose powder), for accuracy in weighing of small amounts of certain ingredients (0·1 lb. of an accelerator is obtained by weighing out 1·0 lb. of a 10% masterbatch) and for improving the dispersion in the rubber of certain materials which are difficult to incorporate easily, analogous to the cook's method of making a smooth custard by first creaming the powder with a little of the liquid before adding the remainder. Since masterbatches are non-productive (a further mixing stage being necessary) the modern tendency is to limit their use and mix direct.

Mixing

At the end of the mixing stage the rubber compound should be homogeneous, every part of the batch being similar in properties to every other part. The correct order and times of adding the compounding ingredients will have been specified by the technical department. These instructions must be followed exactly if the finished batch is to meet the routine batch testing limits. Incorrect order of adding the ingredients may result in local concentrations of sulphur, accelerator and accelerator activators with the possibility of scorching. Little hard lumps of poorly dispersed ingredients may be formed by the addition of oil softeners at the wrong time, with obvious difficulties in the subsequent extrusion or calendering. The specified cooling arrangements must be adhered to, if setting-up in storage is to be avoided. When mixing compound in an internal mixer it is essential to get the batch through the mill nip immediately after dumping, since the heat held by the large pieces of stock will soon result in scorching. During World War II when air raid warnings were frequent and in subsequent years when power cuts interrupted production, most mill rooms had a procedure worked out so that a quick shut-down could be made with the minimum of scorched stock and the minimum of difficulty in getting the process under way again. The drill worked out to cope with these emergencies may still be employed in the case of a mechanical breakdown and a surprising amount of compound can be saved if each member of, say, an extruder or calender gang knows exactly what to do in such an emergency.

To ensure that all the ingredients are present and are homogeneously dispersed in the batch, it is customary to take a small sample, give it a short cure at a high temperature and determine its hardness, its modulus at a certain elongation and its specific gravity. The results obtained are compared with the standards set for the particular mix and batches are accepted or rejected accordingly. In the case of a faulty batch the actual test results will often give a clue as to what has gone wrong with the mixing process and enable correction to be made. Modulus testing has already been mentioned in Chapter V; specific gravity determination will be discussed in Appendix A and hardness measurement in Chapter XIII on 'Testing'.

Warming-up (breaking down)

As we have seen, the uniform delivery of an ample supply of correctly warmed stock is essential to the operations of calendering and extrusion. Mill capacity should be adequate to ensure that there is never any chance of feeding insufficiently warmed stock to the next process. If the slabs of compound have been piled too hot after mixing or held in storage too long before re-use, there is a possibility of scorching which may show itself on the warming mill. The rough appearance of slightly scorched compound may sometimes be mistaken for the 'crow's feet' marking and pitted appearance of compound which is being warmed on a cold mill, but an experienced operative will never be deceived, since the 'handle' of the mix on the mill during cutting and rolling will indicate whether or not scorching is likely.

Calendering

Whatever the type of calendering process — frictioning, coating, sheeting or profiling — an even feed of compound of uniform plasticity is essential. The pendulum feed which distributes the strip evenly across the nip has already been mentioned. Frictioning is a tricky process since the compound must be tacky enough to cling to the centre bowl and soft enough to give good impregnation of the fabric. The ingredients in a calendering mix will determine the range of bowl temperatures over which good results will be obtained. The higher the rubber content of the mix, the higher must be the bowl temperatures, which may range from 100° F for a heavily loaded stock to approximately 200° F for a high rubber content or 'high gum' stock. Where a considerable amount of heat will be stored in the calendered material, e.g. rolls of tyre cord fabric, passing the rubbered cord over a series of cooling drums is necessary to avoid assembly difficulties due to incipient scorch or set-up of the surface. Calendered sheet shows a difference in properties along and across its length. In the direction of calendering it shows high strength but low stretch, while at right angles to the direction in which it leaves the bowls, it may be easily stretched but has poor strength. This effect, termed 'calender grain', may give trouble in later stages of processing, mainly with non-moulded products, since warming of the sheeted rubber relieves the internal stresses and so changes its dimensions. In the manufacture of such articles as football bladders and air cushions a controlled warming, termed 'shrinking', is given the sheet before assembly.

Extrusion

Uniformly warmed stock is again required and plasticity control is advisable since too stiff a mix will run rough and may scorch, while too soft a stock will not run true to dimensions since it tends to slip in the extruder screw. For reasons already explained the recovery value of the mix as well as the plasticity should be held to close limits. In the extrusion of thin tubing, the presence of foreign matter or small lumps of undispersed ingredients may cause scoring or splitting of the product. For such extrusions, sieving of all the ingredients and straining or refining of the mix prior to extruding may be necessary.

Assembly

This term summarises all the various operations which are required for the fashioning of the uncured product — tyre, belting, hose, footwear, etc. The surface tack of the components is thus, by far, the most important property concerned in assembly. To facilitate production it is often required that at one stage rubber surfaces may be laid together without sticking, but at a later stage, contact with the assistance of pressure (by hand or machine) should result in a perfect uncured bond. There are obvious difficulties in meeting these two opposing requirements. Some compounding ingredients, notably sulphur, tend to migrate to the surface of uncured rubber and form a 'bloom' which effectively destroys tack. Both tack and blooming will be discussed in greater detail in Chapters IX and X. Loss of tack may be due to surface set up, one manifestation of the scorch problem, but it is not generally realised that a surface effect akin to pre-curing may result from exposure of the surface to sunlight. Shading of glass roofs in those departments handling uncured compound is therefore advisable, not only for operator comfort but to prevent possible difficulty in assembly.

Processing requirements of rubber compounds in relation to vulcanisation will be dealt with in the next chapter after the various methods of curing have been discussed.

REFERENCE

Vanderbilt Rubber Handbook. 1958, New York, U.S.A., pp. 386–409

CHAPTER VIII

VULCANISATION

The process of sulphur vulcanisation was discovered about 120 years ago and its importance can hardly be over-emphasised. Effects akin to that of vulcanisation can be produced by other means (exposure of the rubber to atomic radiation is the most recent) but sulphur vulcanisation is responsible for the production of all but a minute fraction of the output of rubber articles.

The Science of Vulcanisation

Thomas Hancock writes that the term vulcanisation "owes its derivation to the Vulcan of mythology, as in some degree representing the employment of sulphur and heat, with which that mythological personage was supposed to be familiar". In recent years the meaning of the term has been broadened to include any treatment which brings about an effect similar to that of sulphur vulcanisation, e.g. increased elasticity, reduced plasticity and reduced sensitivity to extremes of heat and cold. Of the process of vulcanisation it may truly be said that the art has outdistanced the science; by that we mean that our knowledge of the methods of vulcanisation far exceeds our understanding of the reasons underlying the process. An enormous amount of scientific work has been carried out in the last century and it has been proved that the sulphur enters into chemical combination with the rubber, but the exact mechanism is not yet known. Although this lack of knowledge has had no apparent effect on the art of vulcanisation, it is well-known that a complete knowledge of the progress of any chemical reaction often leads to improvements in its industrial application.

The change in the molecular structure of rubber resulting from vulcanisation has already been mentioned when we discussed premature vulcanisation (scorching), but it bears repetition. A piece of rubber is visualised as a tangled mass of kinky thread-like molecules. Stretching the unvulcanised material results in pulling the kinks out of the molecules which then begin to slide over each other, since there is nothing joining one molecule to another. When the

74

rubber is vulcanised, however, the sulphur is thought to link up the rubber molecules at many points along their length thus developing the 'snappiness' or elasticity of cured rubber. The chemist calls these linkages simply 'cross-links' or, more picturesquely, 'sulphur bridges'. This essential ingredient is ordinary yellow sulphur, originally obtained from volcanic areas such as the island of Sicily, but, in recent years, produced almost entirely from vast deposits in the U.S.A.

When we discussed compounding ingredients and the development of compounding it was noted that a mix consisting solely of rubber and sulphur, required several hours at a high temperature to give a well-cured product. With the development of accelerators of ever-increasing activity, both the time and temperature of cure have been progressively reduced, with a resultant improvement in quality. Nowadays, in fact, some types of articles require no separate vulcanisation process whatever. These improvements, introduced by the rubber chemists, made it necessary for the engineering staffs to introduce improved cooling of mixing machinery, better temperature control of calenders and extruders, faster operating presses, etc.

The Technology of Vulcanisation

The majority of rubber articles are vulcanised by what might be called the direct method. The sulphur is mixed into the rubber stock, the article or its components are formed by extrusion or calendering, and heat is applied by some suitable means to bring about the rubber-sulphur reaction. Pressure may also be applied if shaping is necessary during the curing operation. In the indirect method of vulcanisation with sulphur, no sulphur as such is mixed with the rubber but it is actually produced during the process from sulphur-containing substances. Thin articles may be vulcanised by the 'cold cure' method; the rubber stock contains no sulphur and after shaping by dipping or spreading, the goods are immersed in a suitably-diluted solution of sulphur monochloride, a liquid substance formed when sulphur reacts with chlorine.

The actual methods of vulcanisation used depend on the type of product and fall into several classes, with a number of variations in each class. It is even possible to use a combination of two classes.

Open Steam Curing

This method is used for those products which do not require the precision of shape given by a mould. The term 'open' is usually taken to indicate that the steam is circulating openly in a pressure vessel or 'autoclave' (a'w-tō-klav). The precise method of supporting the un-cured article during open steam curing varies according to the product. Small diameter cables, rubber tubing and football bladders are embedded in a container filled with soapstone powder; larger cables are coiled on drums and hose is cured on long mandrels with a cloth wrapping to give extra pressure for consolidation. It should not be imagined that the term 'autoclave' is peculiar to the rubber industry. It is defined as "a strong vessel for carrying out chemical reactions under pressure and at high temperatures, or one in which super-heated steam under pressure is used for sterilising or cooking". An autoclave for carrying out the vulcanisation of rubber is often known in the factory simply as a 'vulcaniser', 'heater', 'pan' or even 'tank'. Being pressure vessels, autoclaves are of very robust construction and are subject to the same stringent regulations as for steam boilers. They vary in size, from a small laboratory model right up to one which will contain a railway tank-car. They may be positioned either horizontally or vertically whichever suits the product best. The lid on modern autoclaves is of the 'boltless' type, rotation of the lid by a few degrees causing lugs on the lid to engage with corresponding lugs on the end of the pan. To ensure that temperature is uniform at all parts of the autoclave, the inlet pipes are arranged to distribute the steam as evenly as possible throughout the vessel, which must be fitted with a safety valve, pressure gauge and also steam traps for the efficient removal of condensate (condensed steam). Modern pans are fitted with some system of automatic temperature control which varies the steam supply to maintain the desired temperature and discharges conden-sate as it is formed. Wide temperature variations will result if the air which originally fills the autoclave is not removed and it is advisable to keep the exhaust valve fully open until it is certain that the air has been swept out by the incoming steam. Where very uniform curing is essential, it may be necessary to rotate the articles during cure, e.g. cables on drums, pneumatic tyres remoulded by the 'Vitacap' process.

Before continuing with other vulcanisation techniques, we must digress a little and discuss 'steam' and 'steam pressure', a subject very effectively covered in the Spirax-Sarco Ltd. publication noted at the end of the chapter. Steam is used in industry generally, as a very con-venient source of heat energy and of pressure energy. The rubber industry is concerned mainly with the heat energy, although in open steam curing we rely on the steam exerting a certain pressure on the

Fig. 22. Horizontal autoclave.

articles. Steam is water in the form of a gas — a colourless gas, although the term 'steam' is popularly applied to the clouds of droplets of water which are formed when steam meets the cooler air of the atmosphere. Steam as a heating medium owes its popularity to the following: (i) its excellent heat-carrying capacity, (ii) it may be made from water (which is cheap) heated by a wide variety of fuels, (iii) it may be generated in units of a wide variety of types and sizes (from small electrode boilers to large power station units), (iv) it is piped fairly easily from point of manufacture to point of use, and (v) leaks are easily seen.

A clear distinction must be made between 'heat' and 'temperature' since on the floor of the vulcanising shop the words are often used wrongly. In the simplest terms, 'temperature' is the degree of hotness or coldness of a body; 'heat' is that which when added to a body raises its temperature and when taken away lowers its temperature. Temperature is measured in degrees, the Fahrenheit scale, named after its inventor, being the commonest in industry. In Appendix A the conversion from this scale to the more scientific Centigrade system will be explained. Heat is measured in thermal units, a British Thermal Unit being the quantity of heat required to raise the temperature of 1 lb. of water through 1 Fahrenheit degree. If we take some water just at freezing point (32° F) and apply heat to it, we can follow the effect of the heating by watching the steady rising of the mercury column of a thermometer inserted in the liquid. The temperature will rise from 32° F to 212° F at which point the water will boil. If we continue heating, there will be no further rise in temperature, (provided the vessel is open to the atmosphere) and eventually the water will all boil off as steam. The heat supplied to bring about the rise in temperature from 32° F to 212° F is the 'Sensible Heat' ('sensed' or 'felt' by the thermometer) while that amount of heat which brought about the change of state from liquid to gas is the Latent Heat ('concealed' or 'dormant'). The reason why we cannot raise the temperature of the water in an open vessel above 212° F is that we have added sufficient heat energy to the water molecules to enable them to overcome the pressure of the atmosphere and so escape as gas. Atmospheric pressure is the pressure exerted by the envelope of air in which the world is enclosed and which extends upwards for about a hundred miles. At sea level the weight of the column of air standing on one square inch of surface is about 14·7 lb. i.e., atmospheric pressure at sea level is 14·7 p.s.i. Since the higher up this column of air we go, the less is the weight of air above, it is obvious that atmospheric pressure decreases with altitude. This has important consequences — high flying aircraft must be pressurised — but the most interesting one in the present connection is that at high altitudes water 'boils' at a temperature which is too low to enable cooking to be done — potatoes will not soften, eggs will not 'boil' and good tea cannot be brewed. Mountaineers therefore take along small autoclaves, better known as pressure cookers, to enable such meals to be prepared.

We will go further with our water heating example and consider what happens if we use a sealed vessel or small boiler equipped with a thermometer and a pressure gauge. A pressure gauge is simply a device fitted with a specially-shaped narrow bore tube which coils and uncoils as pressure varies, the movement of the tube being geared to a pointer which travels over a graduated dial. The standard pressure gauge used in steam work really reads pressure above atmospheric pressure, which is all that concerns us in the factory; to get the true or 'absolute pressure' we would have to add 14·7 to the indicated gauge reading. Continued heating of the water in the boiler after 212° F is reached results in a further temperature rise, since the closing of the vessel has contained the fast-moving molecules and the heat energy they are receiving is showing itself by a larger number of impacts on the walls of the boiler, i.e. by increased pressure. Taking readings of gauge pressure and corresponding temperature, we get a table which might look as follows:

Gauge Pressure (p.s.i.)	Temperature (° F)
0	212
10	239
20	258
30	274
40	287
50	298
60	307
70	316
80	324
90	330

Although it must be accepted as industry usage, it is nevertheless very unfortunate that curing conditions are often quoted in terms of pressure instead of temperature, e.g. 30 min. at 40 lb. steam. What this really means is, 30 min. at the temperature corresponding to the pressure of 40 p.s.i. steam. You already know one very good reason for not assuming that a pressure gauge reading of 40 p.s.i. means a temperature of 287° F — an autoclave used at the altitude of, say, Mexico City (7,500 ft. above sea-level) would have a temperature of only 282° F for this gauge reading. The presence of air in an open steam heater (not removed at beginning of cure, leakage from the air-bags used in curing tyres, or deliberately introduced to give increased pressure without increased temperature) will all play havoc with the normal equivalence of steam pressure and temperature. The misuse of steam pressure for temperature has even been carried over to vulcanising equipment which does not use steam at all, e.g. 30 min. at 40 lb. (steam) in a moulding press with electrically-heated platens.

Before leaving open steam curing we must consider some properties of rubber which are of great importance in the curing by heat of all but the thinnest of rubber articles. We have often mentioned time and temperature of cure but have not so far related the thickness of the product to these two factors. The best or optimum cure for a particular compound is selected on the basis of tests made on fairly thin test-pieces, say $\frac{1}{16}$ in. to $\frac{1}{8}$ in., which attain the specified temperature almost instantaneously. It should be noted that the optimum cure does not necessarily mean selecting the best value of any particular property, for reasons which will be dealt with under 'Physical Testing'. Rubber is a very poor conductor of heat and it is difficult to produce an even state of cure throughout a thick article. In a few cases we may apply heat to both sides, as in the vulcanising of pneumatic tyres where steam or hot water is supplied to the diaphragm or curing bag which provides the internal moulding pressure. The use of organic accelerators has assisted greatly in making more even the rate of cure of heavy products and the application of heat to the outside of the article for a time long enough to cure the inside does not now result in severe overcure of the outside. The ideal to be aimed at in all forms of heat vulcanisation is for the scorch rate and cure rate of the compound, the time and temperature of cure and the pressure applied, to be so inter-related that the rubber is warmed uniformly throughout and all the desired flow has taken place before any structure due to the cross-linking of the molecules is developed. In open steam curing a useful way of bringing the inside of a product slowly up to curing temperature is to specify a 'rise' period before the 'cure' period proper, e.g. a cure written 45/120 min. at 287° F indicates that the pan temperature increases steadily from room temperature up to 287° F, after which it is held steady at 287° F for a further period of 120 min. A 'drop' period may even be desirable at the end of the steady or 'hold' period. A 'step' cure is a development of the 'rise' type of cure, a series of 'rises' and 'holds' being given before the final cure temperature is reached. These procedures sound very involved but are carried out efficiently with the aid of time/temperature controllers which will be described when we discuss 'Instrumentation and Automatic Control'.

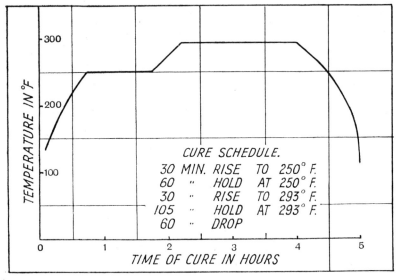

CURE SCHEDULE.
30 MIN. RISE TO 250° F.
60 " HOLD AT 250° F.
30 " RISE TO 293° F.
105 " HOLD AT 293° F.
60 " DROP

FIG. 23.   Step cure.

Press Curing

While the two halves of a mould may be bolted together and used in an autoclave, moulded articles are usually produced from some kind of press, an arrangement of heated tables or 'platens' which close on the mould and hold it shut by 'hydraulic' pressure. As the name 'hydraulic' indicates, water is the usual liquid employed to produce the pressure but oil may also be used. The principles behind the operation of any hydraulic mechanism be it lift, crane, press or garage jack, can be studied in any physics text book (see references at end of chapter). The main features of a rubber moulding press are shown in Fig. 24. The cross-head which carries the top platen is fixed and remains stationary. The moving table or lower platen is forced upwards by means of hydraulic pressure admitted into the cylinder below the ram. Around the ram are a gland and packing ring which permit the ram to move freely up and down without loss of the hydraulic fluid. In this up-stroking press the ram is raised by hydraulic pressure and falls by gravity, but down-stroking types are available in which the top table moves downwards to apply the pressure to the

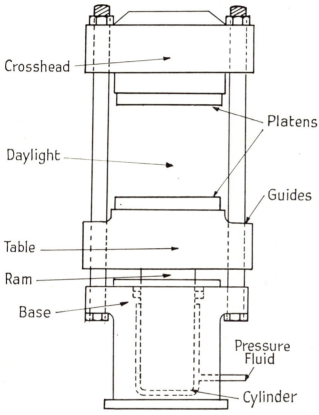

Crosshead

Platens

Daylight

Guides

Table

Ram

Base

Pressure Fluid

Cylinder

FIG. 24.   Hydraulic moulding press.

mould and auxiliary rams are provided to raise it. The space between the platens is termed a 'daylight', the press shown being a single daylight type as it takes only one mould or one set of moulds of the same height. More platens may be provided giving an increase in the number of daylights and thus in the number of moulds which can be accommodated. Platens may be heated by steam, oil or electricity, the specified temperature being maintained preferably by an automatic control system. The capacity of a press is the total tonnage it is capable of exerting on the moulds and is determined by the area of the ram and the pressure attainable from the hydraulic system. A laboratory type bench press with a hand pump for producing the pressure may have a capacity of only 5 tons. At the other end of the scale a large press, such as is used in the vulcanisation of belting, may have platens 30 ft. long by 5 ft. wide, operated by 8 rams exerting a total force of over 3,000 tons. The required hydraulic pressure of about 2,000 p.s.i. in such cases is obtained from a battery of electrically-driven pumps. For the efficient moulding of rubber a pressure of about $\frac{1}{2}$ ton per sq. in. of mould surface is required and it is important to ensure that press capacities are ample to maintain this pressure throughout the cure. Hydraulic fluid is often supplied at two pressures, a low pressure of, say, 500 p.s.i. for raising the ram and a high pressure of about 2,000 p.s.i. for the actual moulding. The pumps are usually connected to an 'accumulator', a device similar in principle to a hydraulic press, with a heavily-weighted ram which stores water under pressure and releases it when there is a sudden demand for more pressure than can be provided by the pumps. Calculations relating to mould areas and press capacities will be found in Appendix A.

The basic press just described has been modified in a number of ways with the object of producing moulded goods of better quality at greater speed. The modifications are often dictated by the type of product being made — for instance open sided or 'gooseneck' presses are used for V-belts, whereas tilting head presses are used for small moulded articles. Moulds may be fixed to the platens, the opening of the press thus opening the mould, as in the specialised air-operated press for the curing of inner tubes (Fig. 26).

Placing an uncured 'blank' or 'slug' of rubber compound into the bottom half of a mould, fitting the top half, placing the mould in a press and applying pressure is termed simple 'compression' moulding. There are two other methods which have certain advantages in particular applications. These new methods are 'transfer' moulding and 'injection' moulding. In transfer moulding the mould has an upper cavity into which the raw stock is placed, the closing of the mould transfers the rubber through a series of holes into the actual moulding cavity (Fig. 25). For moulding composite articles with metal inserts, transfer moulding is particularly advantageous, since there is less chance of displacing the insert, than with ordinary compression moulding. The idea of injection moulding of rubber was borrowed from the plastics industry. The method is akin to extrusion, the rubber being forced by a screw to the head of the machine, to which the mould is clamped. When one mould is filled it is removed and replaced by another. The method is automatic and gives an immense output of small mouldings.

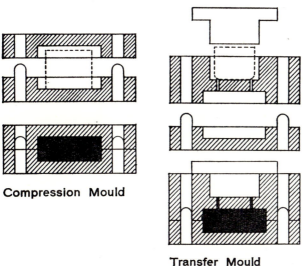

Compression Mould

Transfer Mould

FIG. 25.   Compression and transfer moulding.

Moulds are made of a variety of materials, depending on the use and the conditions of moulding. Cast iron and steel are the commonest materials for ordinary work. Moulds made of ebonite may be used for articles such as cash mats; the method of manufacture consists of pressing a cured mat into a slab of uncured ebonite, giving it a short cure until the mat can be stripped off, and then completing the cure until the ebonite is hard enough to be used as a mould. Rubber-stamp makers use moulds of plaster, in hand-screw presses. For heels and tiles white metal moulds are common, the metal being an alloy of lead and antimony, which may be melted down and recast when the mould becomes off-size or damaged in any way. Flexible moulds of certain synthetic resins are becoming popular for short runs.

In the moulding process it must be remembered that shaping and curing are being done at one and the same time. It is obvious that the rubber must flow and take the shape of the mould before the actual vulcanisation reaction commences. This is extremely important in precision moulding, since any structure developed before moulding pressure is applied will cause a variation in shrinkage after the product is removed from the mould. In my own experience delay in applying pressure to a mould containing tensile test slabs permitted so much cure structure to develop that the slabs curled up and actually sprang out of the mould as soon as the top half was removed. There must be sufficient stock in the mould to fill it, otherwise the cured article will be what is termed 'light', i.e. corners will be rounded when they should be sharp, and the article may show porosity either on the surface or internally. While moulds are provided with a spue-ring to take a small amount of overflow, the amount of stock in the mould must not be excessive or the two halves may be held open and produce a very ugly rind on the cured article. With thick products it is extremely important that the curing temperature should not be high enough to cause the surface to set up before the inside of the article has warmed up and expanded. If the surface is partly cured, no flow can take place, and the force of the expanding interior will open the mould, even against a high hydraulic pressure, and result in severe splitting of the cured job along the line of the mould register. In designing moulds, it is useful to remember that the expansion of rubber due to heating (its 'thermal' expansion) is very much higher than that of most other solid materials. It is approximately twenty times greater than the steel of which most moulds are made.

A basic principle in moulding is to arrange the shape of the raw article so that the air in the mould is driven out before it can be trapped. In intricate designs, such as the treads of pneumatic tyres, this is not possible and it is necessary to cut little holes or 'vents' right through the mould to get rid of trapped air. The ribbed and diamond designs on some mats and hot-water bottles are there to help trapped air to escape, rather than for appearance.

Autoclave Press Curing

This method of curing is a combination of the open steam and the press curing methods, and has its greatest application in the vulcanisation of pneumatic tyres. The autoclave press is a strong steel cylinder, set vertically, and provided with a hydraulically-operated ram, boltless type lid, safety valve and valve for blowing out air at the start of a cure. The dimensions of the cylinder depend on the sizes of tyres to be cured. A time-temperature-condensation control system is invariably fitted, by means of which the temperature of cure may be

Fig. 26.   Curing tyre inner tubes.

kept at any desired level (a 'rise' and 'drop' may also be arranged), the condensate is removed as soon as it is formed, and the timing of the cure, once set, is automatically carried out. The moulds are simply stacked one on top of the other, the pressure to hold them shut being applied by the hydraulic ram pushing the column of moulds against the lid of the autoclave. The heat for curing is supplied by admitting steam under pressure, which circulates round the moulds. Since a pneumatic tyre is not solid, but merely a casing, a heavy type of inner tube, termed a curing bag, is fitted inside the raw cover. When the bag is inflated with air or steam, the pressure forces the uncured rubber against the engraving on the mould and produces the tread pattern, in addition to consolidating the whole assembly while the vulcanisation reaction is in progress.

Hot Air Curing

This method is mainly used for the curing of some types of foot-wear. To obtain the very high finish, these articles are lacquered before curing, and the drying of the lacquer is completed during the cure. The hot air method may also be used for some proofed cloths. The vulcaniser is double-walled, the heat for curing being obtained from steam circulating between the two walls. Blistering of hot air-cured goods is lessened if the air in the vulcaniser is under pressure, 15 to 40 p.s.i. being the usual range. To ensure even heating it is customary to circulate the air by a fan, or to rotate the racks holding the articles. Since steam does not come in contact with the goods, this method is sometimes referred to as the 'dry heat' cure.

Cold Curing

This process is used for the vulcanisation of dipped goods produced from rubber solution (bottle teats, surgeons' gloves) and proofed cloth made by the spreading method. No sulphur is added to the mix from which the dipping solution or spreading dough is made, the curing effect being obtained by exposing the articles to the action of sulphur monochloride, diluted with a petroleum solvent. Dipped goods are immersed in the solution for a time which depends on the thickness of the article, and proofed cloth is vulcanised by passing it over a roller which runs in a trough of the curing solution. The cloth rotates the roller which picks up the solution and transfers it to the face of the proofing. Sulphur monochloride reacts with moisture (present in the atmosphere) to produce hydrochloric acid, which if left on the articles would result in poor ageing of the rubber and rotting ('tendering') of the fabric. Cold cured goods are, therefore, treated with an alkaline substance, usually ammonia, to neutralise any acid that might be present, the process being known as 'sweetening'.

Vapour curing is a variation of the cold cure method, the vapour being that of sulphur monochloride. Since the penetration of the vapour is less than that of cold cure solution, the limiting thickness for articles to be cured in this way is about 0·040 in.

Sulphur monochloride is a very obnoxious liquid, as is carbon disulphide, which was commonly used, until its prohibition a few years ago, as the solvent in making up the cold cure solution. In view of the stringent precautions necessary to safeguard the health of the operatives using these liquids and the advent of very fast (ultra) accelerators, both cold curing and vapour curing are obsolescent.

If these basic vulcanising techniques are grasped, you will have no difficulty in understanding the variations and combinations of methods which will be met with in practice. As already noted, a mould normally used in an hydraulic press may have its two halves bolted firmly together and be used in an autoclave. A moulded article may be given a short cure in a press, removed from the mould and the cure completed in an autoclave. A continuous curing method is becoming popular for cables, the wire conductor being covered with rubber by extrusion and then led straight into a tube 100 to 200 ft. long containing steam at a pressure of about 200 p.s.i. Continuous curing of belting and flooring will be described in Chapter XII. Where it is impossible to use any 'factory' curing method such as in belt repairing on site, cable splicing, tyre repairing, etc., portable electrically heated units or infra-red lamps may be employed, in conjunction with fast-curing rubber compounds. These repair compounds may have to be kept in stock for many months or even years before use with consequent risk of setting-up. In such cases and especially where no heat for curing is available or desirable, the 'split batch' technique is useful. Two compounds are supplied, generally in the form of a stiff dough, one containing the sulphur, the other the accelerator. Just before use, equal parts of the two doughs are taken and thoroughly kneaded together, thus giving a mix which will vulcanise at normal temperature in as short a time as twenty-four hours. Such methods used in the repair of tyres are now popularly, but erroneously, being referred to as 'chemical' curing.

REFERENCES

POWELL, L. S., *Elementary Physics for Technical Students*. London

SEAMEN, R. G. and MERRILL, A. M., Machinery and Equipment for Rubber and Plastics. *Rubber World*. Vol. I, New York, U.S.A.

Folio I. Spirax-Sarco Ltd., Cheltenham, Glos.

CHAPTER IX

COMPOUNDING INGREDIENTS, I

In Chapter V we introduced you to the compounding of rubber by describing the sort of properties the customer requires, and Chapter VII indicated the properties required for satisfactory processing. We are now almost ready to discuss in detail the multitude of ingredients added to rubber to satisfy these two fundamental demands.

Of the ninety-two elementary substances, or elements, of which the universe is composed, the rubber industry regularly uses some twenty-five in either their elementary or uncombined form, such as carbon black and sulphur, or combined with other elements as in zinc oxide, titanium dioxide, calcium carbonate, iron oxide, chromium oxide, barium sulphate, etc. For those readers training as technicians a deep knowledge of chemistry is not required, but much more will be gained from this and the following chapter if some acquaintance has been made with one of the many excellent texts now available (see references at end of chapter). The length and seeming complexity of the names given to many organic chemicals have already been noted. In a book at this level of instruction some of these names must be shirked in favour of well-known and accepted abbreviations. Professor Read's book can be recommended to those interested in knowing how these names are derived. Another branch of science — physics — and in particular that section dealing with density and specific gravity, is essential for a proper understanding of compounding. Since this is not handled by physics text-books in a manner to suit our particular needs, it will be dealt with in Chapter X when we discuss that group of compounding ingredients known as fillers.

Classification of Compounding Ingredients

Before the functions of compounding ingredients were fully understood there was little point in attempting to classify them. Now that compounding is less a matter of 'rule of thumb' a scientific grouping is possible. The following scheme is adapted from *The Fundamentals of Rubber Technology* noted in the references.

88

1. Elastomers. (*a*) Natural. (*b*) Synthetic. (*c*) Reclaim.
2. Peptising agents.
3. Vulcanising agents. (*a*) Sulphur, (*b*) Sulphur-containing, (*c*) Other materials.
4. Accelerators. (*a*) Medium. (*b*) Fast. (*c*) Ultra.
5. Activators. (*a*) Inorganic. (*b*) Organic.
6. Fillers. (*a*) Reinforcing (i) Black
                    (ii) Non-Black.
    (*b*) Extending.
7. Softeners. (*a*) Processing aid. (*b*) Extender.
8. Protective agents. (*a*) Antioxidants and antiozonants. (*b*) Physical.
9. Special components. (*a*) Blowing agents for sponge. (*b*) Abrasives. (*c*) Colours. (*d*) Retarders. (*e*) Flame-proofing agents.

Groups 3, 4 and 5 comprise the curing system or 'curatives'.

To illustrate how these are used in a typical compound, here is the formula for a natural rubber inner tube stock. The abbreviations MBT, TMT and PBN should be disregarded for the moment — an explanation will be given later.

Ingredient	Parts by Weight	Function
Smoked sheet rubber	100·0	Natural elastomer
Sulphur	1·0	Vulcanising agent
MBT	1·0	Accelerator, primary
TMT	0·1	Accelerator, secondary
Zinc Oxide	5·0	Activator, inorganic
Stearic Acid	1·5	Activator, organic
Thermal Black	40·0	Reinforcing filler, black
Mineral Oil	1·5	Softener
PBN	2·0	Antioxidant
	152·1	

This formula expresses the ingredients in relation to 100 parts of rubber (abbreviated to PHR, parts per hundred of rubber). It is the most logical way of writing a rubber compound formula since the ingredients can be considered as reacting with or modifying a standard 100 parts of rubber. This PHR form is sometimes stated as '% on the rubber' but this is not recommended as confusion is possible with '% of the batch weight'. The units of weight may be any convenient unit (pounds, kilograms, grams) and the entire formula may be multiplied or divided as necessary so long as their relationship remains as in the original formula. It is most unlikely that this mix formula would be given as it stands to the department responsible for assembling the components ('putting up' the batch is the shop floor expression), since the volume represented by the weight unit chosen might not suit the open mill or internal mixer to be used. A black masterbatch may be used instead of loose black and the small amount of the secondary accelerator would certainly be weighed out as a masterbatch. Quite a lot of simple arithmetic is usually necessary before the formula can be passed to the factory. Another way of writing a formulation is to express it in percentages, i.e. each ingredient weight is a percentage of the total weight which is of course one hundred. Here is the inner tube formula expressed in this way.

Ingredient	%
Smoked sheet rubber	65·746
Sulphur	0·657
MBT	0·657
TMT	0·066
Zinc Oxide	3·288
Stearic acid	0·986
Thermal black	26·300
Mineral oil	0·986
PBN	1·314
	100·000

Many compound designers use this percentage method exclusively, since some specifications demand a definite rubber content — 40%, 50% or 60%. The method is convenient in budgeting, for calculating say, the quantity of any or all of the ingredients necessary for mixing a given amount of compound. Formulas should really be written in both ways but the student would be well advised to concentrate first on the PHR form, which, from the above example, is obviously much easier to learn, and which tells almost at a glance the type of compound.

We are now ready to deal with individual groups of ingredients (as outlined in the classification system given above), which make up the thousands of ingredients at present available for the compounding of rubber. The present chapter will discuss Groups 1 to 5. It should be pointed out, however, that such classification is not absolute. Many ingredients have a dual function, for example the accelerator MBT can also act as a peptising agent. Some behave differently in synthetic and in natural rubber, for example zinc oxide is the vulcanising agent for neoprene and either the 'accelerator activator' or white 'reinforcing filler' for natural rubber. The classification may change depending on the quantities used (small amounts of oils are 'processing aids', large amounts are extenders) and so on.

GROUP 1. ELASTOMER

(a) Natural

The different types and grades of natural rubber have already been dealt with in Chapter III.

(b) Synthetic

We have dealt in detail with synthetic rubbers in Chapter IV but, for completeness, a brief outline of the main types is repeated here. Since it will be many years, if ever, before the new A.S.T.M. system of nomenclature is fully adopted, we will refer to the various elastomers by their commonly-used names. In general, the compounding of synthetics follows the same pattern as for natural rubber — differences will be pointed out as we come to them.

SBR. This is styrene-butadiene (stī'rēn, bū-ta-dī'-ēn) rubber named from the organic chemicals of which it is composed. It was formerly known as GR-S (Government Rubber-Styrene) and is a general purpose rubber mainly used in the treads of pneumatic tyres. The abbreviations LTP and OEP both refer to SB rubbers; LTP is a low temperature polymer or 'cold' rubber since it is made by a reaction carried out at a lower temperature (41° F) than that at which the original GR-S was made (122° F). OEP denotes oil extended polymer since there is an addition of oil during the manufacture of the rubber.

Butyl. This was originally a special purpose rubber noted for its very low permeability to air and other gases. It finds its greatest use in pneumatic tyre inner tubes and similar applications. It has excellent resistance to attack by ozone, and is being developed for many uses in which resistance to weathering is required.

Nitrile rubber. This rubber has extremely high resistance to attack by oil and is therefore used in making oil seals, gaskets, and similar products.

Neoprene. This also has good oil resistance combined with excellent resistance to weathering.

Silicone rubber. The outstanding feature of this synthetic is its resistance to extremes of temperature. It remains flexible at temperatures as low as − 80° F and can withstand heating for long periods at temperatures up to 500° F without great loss of physical properties.

It should be emphasised that the above terms — SBR, butyl, neoprene, etc., are class names and there are dozens of different types of elastomers in each class. New synthetic elastomers are announced with surprising regularity but most are not in bulk production. Reference to some of the most important of these has been made in Chapter IV.

(c) Reclaim

Many rubber articles which have ended their useful lives are subjected to the action of chemicals, treated with steam at high temperature and, after the addition of oils, are replasticised by mechanical working. Such reclaimed rubber is a useful compounding ingredient since it is already plasticised and thus lowers the power consumption during mixing. The price of reclaim remains very steady and shows none of the wide price variations to which natural rubber is subject. The rubber content of reclaim is about 50%, the remainder being fillers, oils, etc. Whole tyre reclaim, the most popular type, contains about 10% of carbon black, and the use of this material, suitably compounded, is a good way of introducing part of the carbon black content to a compound.

Reclaim is made by several methods — acid process, alkali process, neutral process — depending on the chemicals used. In general, the scrap rubber is reduced to a size suitable for the particular process by mechanical chopping or by cracking on a very heavy cracker mill. The textile portion of the article, if any, is destroyed by chemical treatment, or by heating, and the scrap is then treated in an autoclave for several hours at a high temperature. Washing, drying, addition of oils, straining through a fine mesh gauze and finally sheeting very thinly on a refiner mill complete the process. Other less well-known methods of reclaiming are described by Stafford and Wright (see references at end of chapter). Reclaiming does not devulcanise the rubber, but merely replasticises it, and the product must not be confused with vulcanised crumb rubber, which is made by simply grinding down vulcanised waste to a size which makes it suitable for addition, as a filler, to a new compound.

GROUP 2. PEPTISING AGENTS

These materials are used to assist the breaking down of natural rubber and some synthetic rubbers, prior to the incorporation of other compounding ingredients. It is thought that a conventional

FIG. 27.   Final sheeting of reclaimed rubber.

softener for rubber functions by working its way between the long-chain molecules and thus almost acts as a lubricant, the effect being mainly physical. A chemical plasticiser or 'peptiser' exerts a chemical action on the molecular chains which have been broken by mechanical working and prevents the broken sections from recombining. Unlike conventional softeners, peptisers do not soften the vulcanised product to any appreciable extent. Very small amounts of peptising agents result in considerable saving of time and power during the costly breaking-down operation. Peptisers are complex organic sulphur-containing substances, which will here be referred to by their trade names. Pepton 22 and Vulcamel TBN are most effective under conditions of 'hot' mastication in internal mixers, i.e. at temperatures above 220° F; Pepton 65 is active at as low a temperature as 160° F and is thus suitable for use during open mill mastication. The quantities required are 0·2 to 0·5 PHR for natural rubber and between 1·0 and 2·0 PHR for SBR. The accelerator MBT has a peptising effect under hot mastication conditions, 0·5 PHR often being added during pre-mastication. The amount so added must be taken into account, of course, by reducing the MBT added as an accelerator in the final mix.

GROUP 3. VULCANISING AGENTS

(a) Sulphur

Although there are quite a number of substances which will bring about vulcanisation of rubber, the only one of commercial importance is ordinary yellow sulphur. The greater part of this sulphur is obtained from the U.S.A., where large deposits exist in Louisiana and Texas. The sulphur lies beneath about 900 ft. of clay, sand and rock and cannot be brought to the surface by conventional mining methods. It is obtained by an ingenious process, the 'Frasch' process (named after its discoverer), in which a series of concentric pipes is sunk down to the sulphur deposit. Superheated water is passed down to melt the sulphur which is then forced to the surface by compressed air. The molten sulphur is allowed to cool and later ground to the required fineness. Sicily is the great historic source of sulphur, but its production is now relatively insignificant. Here it was obtained by mining and purified by melting and recooling.

In 1951 the export of sulphur from the U.S.A. was restricted and work was started in the U.K. on the recovery of sulphur from sources not considered profitable in normal circumstances. Recovery from petroleum refining was the most successful of these projects.

Ordinary sulphur is soluble in rubber to some extent and, if the amount of sulphur in the mix exceeds 1 PHR, 'blooming' of the surface of the uncured rubber will result. 'Bloom' and 'blooming' are terms denoting the appearance on the surface of either uncured or cured rubber of any compounding ingredient. Sulphur and certain

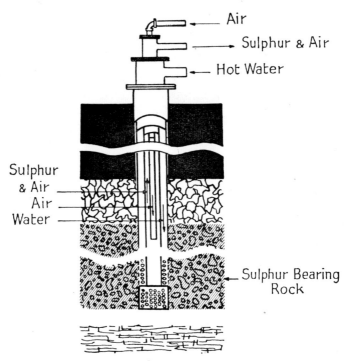

FIG. 28.   'Frasch' process.

waxes are the substances commonly referred to, when blooming is discussed, but the effect is not confined to these.

Most rubber compounds need from 2·0 to 3·0 PHR of sulphur to effect vulcanisation, an amount which is more than the rubber will hold in solution. Sulphur bloom on uncured rubber leads to loss of building tack, which will give difficulty in assembly, although there are processes for which a slight bloom is welcomed since it allows one uncured component to be stacked on another without the use of a lining or other means of separation. Sulphur bloom on cured rubber generally indicates that the product is undercured.

Sulphur exists in a number of different physical forms, one of which is insoluble in rubber and therefore does not migrate (through continued solution and re-crystallisation) to the surface of the rubber. Such 'insoluble sulphurs' containing varying percentages of the insoluble form are on the market under several trade names. They are used in rubbers which have to be stocked for some considerable time in the uncured state, e.g. tyre and tube repair gums, tread rubber (camelback) for retreading tyres. The heat of vulcanisation converts such insoluble sulphur back to the ordinary form and there is no adverse effect on cure. Insoluble sulphur is more expensive than ordinary sulphur and therefore it is not usual to use it exclusively — it may be mixed in any proportion with the ordinary variety. Compounds containing insoluble sulphur should be processed at temperatures not exceeding 220° F to prevent reversion to the more stable ordinary sulphur. Insoluble sulphur should not be stored for long periods before use, since even at normal temperatures some degree of reversion takes place.

(b) Sulphur-containing

The most important of these is sulphur monochloride, used in solution with solvent naphtha for the vulcanisation of sheeting and other thin articles by the 'cold cure' process. No sulphur is added to the mix, the vulcanisation being brought about by the absorption of the sulphur monochloride into the article.

Tetramethylthiuram disulphide (TMT), best known as an ultra accelerator, may be used as a vulcanising agent without the addition of any elemental sulphur, since at curing temperatures TMT liberates sulphur in very active form. 2·0 to 4·0 PHR of TMT are required which adds to the cost of the compound, but the advantages are high resistance to ageing and non-tarnishing of metals, both desirable features in cable stocks.

(c) Other materials

The elements selenium and tellurium, which belong to the same chemical family as sulphur, may also be used as vulcanising agents, but they are more frequently employed as secondary vulcanising agents along with sulphur and an accelerator. We have already mentioned that the vulcanising agent for neoprene is a metallic oxide, usually zinc. Butyl rubber may be cured with conventional curatives but is often vulcanised with derivatives of quinone, in conjunction with red lead. Silicone rubbers are cured by the use of certain organic peroxides, such as benzoyl peroxide, and another peroxide, dicumyl peroxide, shows promise also as a non-sulphur vulcanising agent for natural rubber.

GROUP 4. ACCELERATORS

In Chapter V we have already learnt that accelerators are materials used to speed up the reaction of rubber with sulphur. Their use results in better physical properties and improved ageing resistance. The shorter cure time gives greater output due to the quicker turn-round of equipment and, especially in thick articles, greater uniformity of cure throughout the mass. Before discussing accelerators in detail, a few terms relating to the curing characteristics of rubber compounds must first be explained. In making a laboratory evaluation of the tensile properties of a compound, a number of samples are vulcanised at a specified temperature, but at different times, so chosen to range from undercure to overcure. The particular property is measured (by methods which will be given in Chapter XIII) and the results displayed in the form of a graph, with the time scale on the horizontal axis and the units in which we are making the measurement on the vertical axis. Fig. 29 shows the result of such a determination on two different compounds — for simplicity only the

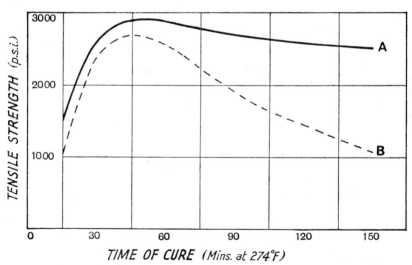

FIG. 29.   Comparison of flat-curing and peaky compounds.

tensile strength curves are given. It will be noted that Curve A falls away very slowly indeed once it has reached its maximum value, the tensile strength for a cure time of 120 min. being only a little below that for 60 min. Such a compound is said to have 'flat curing' characteristics or to show a 'plateau' effect, both terms describing the shape of the curve after it has reached the maximum value. Curve B shows a very sharp drop immediately the maximum has been reached and the curing characteristics are therefore described as 'peaky'. One important advantage of compounds showing a pronounced plateau effect has already been mentioned, namely that thick articles may be adequately cured on the inside without serious degradation of the surface. You will note from Curve A that, on the basis of the laboratory results on thin test pieces, a good technical cure would be 60 min. at 274° F. It is not easy to write a factory curing schedule which will ensure that a variety of types and sizes of products comprising say, an autoclave load, will receive a uniform cure equivalent to this laboratory cure. Compounds having flat-curing characteristics allow a greater amount of latitude in this respect. The compounder achieves this flat-curing effect by choice of type and amount of accelerator, or combination of accelerators, and by balancing suitably the amounts of the other components of the curing system.

Inorganic accelerators such as lime, magnesia and litharge, and the slow-curing organic accelerators are of little practical importance at the present day and will not be considered further. Organic accelerators may be classed in two ways, by chemical composition or by the speed with which they accelerate the rubber-sulphur reaction. We will adopt the latter scheme since it is of greater practical value. Speed is a relative term, however, and even now some factories will class as impossibly fast an accelerator used without trouble in another factory. For reasons given in Chapter VII, safety in processing is just as important as speed of cure. This fact is well illustrated by the development of 'delayed action' accelerators, which are relatively inactive at processing temperatures but which exert their full effect at curing temperatures.

(a) Medium

Diphenylguanidine (DPG) is a typical example of this group. It is still quite popular mainly as a secondary accelerator along with MBT. DPG does not have particularly good ageing properties and tends to give a yellowish tint to white compounds.

H   C.R.T.

(*b*) *Fast*

Mercaptobenzothiazole (MBT) is a general purpose accelerator of wide application. It gives excellent tensile strength with a pronounced plateau effect; ageing and abrasion resistance are excellent. Where required it may be speeded up ('boosted') with TMT, a useful combination being 1·0 PHR of MBT, 0·1 PHR of TMT and 1·5 PHR of sulphur.

Dibenzthiazyldisulphide (MBTS) has properties similar to MBT but gives safer processing.

MBT was the accelerator generally used in pneumatic tyre tread stocks until the introduction of furnace carbon blacks which are made in the U.K. from imported oils. These were found much more scorchy than American channel blacks and a safer accelerator has become popular in this application. Chemically it is cyclohexyl benzthiazyl sulphenamide, usually abbreviated to CBS (trade names — Santocure, Vulcafor HBS). CBS itself was still found scorchy with some newer varieties of furnace blacks and (typical of the service given by the chemical industry to the rubber industry) one manufacturer alone has developed three safer variations during the past few years.

(*c*) *Ultra*

Tetramethylthiuram disulphide (TMT), a typical ultra accelerator, has already been mentioned under 'Vulcanising Agents'. It is non-staining and can be used in white and light-coloured compounds, but precautions against scorching are necessary. In the production of articles direct from latex, heat is not required during processing and ultra accelerators may be used without any scorch problem. Zinc diethyl dithiocarbamate (ZDC) is one of many such accelerators used in this application. Other dry rubber uses of ultra accelerators are in hot air vulcanisation and in self-curing solutions and doughs, where it may be advisable to use the 'split batch' technique mentioned in Chapter VIII.

GROUP 5. ACTIVATORS

(*a*) *Inorganic*

As has been explained in the development of compounding, the rubber/sulphur/accelerator complex requires an activator. Zinc oxide is the most commonly used inorganic activator, the quantity needed being from 3·0 to 5·0 PHR. The method of manufacture of zinc oxide and its use as a white reinforcing filler will be discussed later.

(b) Organic

Variation in the cure rate of raw rubber is known to result from a deficiency of fatty acids in the rubber itself. It is therefore customary to add from 1·0 to 3·0 PHR of stearic acid to most natural rubber compounds, especially those containing an MBT type of accelerator. Stearic (stē-ar'ik) acid is a tallow-like substance obtained from animal fats and should not be confused with mineral acids, such as sulphuric acid.

REFERENCES

UVAROV, E. B. and CHAPMAN, D. R., A Dictionary of Science. Penguin Books Ltd.

HUTTON, KENNETH, Chemistry. Penguin Books Ltd.

READ, JOHN, A Direct Entry to Organic Chemistry. London

The Fundamentals of Rubber Technology. Chap. 4, Imperial Chemical Industries, Dyestuffs Division, Manchester

STAFFORD, W. E. and WRIGHT, R. A., Reclaimed Rubber: Its Manufacture and Uses. Proc. Inst. Rubber Ind. 1954, Vol. 1, 40

CHAPTER X

COMPOUNDING INGREDIENTS, II

GROUP 6. FILLERS

A compound formulation consisting only of the elastomer and sufficient curatives to bring about vulcanisation is called a 'pure gum' mix, the addition of fillers being termed 'loading' the compound. If we desire to enhance certain properties we add reinforcing fillers; if we merely wish to increase the volume of the compound and so reduce its cost, we use 'extending' fillers or 'cheapeners'. Group 6 is therefore divided into two sub-groups and reinforcing fillers are further split into 'black' and 'non-black' types. The loading of an extending filler may be as high as the mix will stand without losing its rubbery feel provided the service requirements are still met, but for reinforcing fillers there is a definite maximum loading for the best reinforcement. Further, the addition of larger quantities of a poor reinforcing filler cannot add to the reinforcement of the mix — if greater reinforcement is needed a better filler must be used. The reinforcement of rubber is a complex property but may be defined as the enhancement of tensile strength, tear strength and abrasion resistance. As with the selection of the best or 'optimum' cure of a rubber compound, the optimum reinforcement based on one or other of the above properties may not suit all service conditions.

Only some finely divided powders have this beneficial effect and as yet we do not know precisely the mechanism of the effect. In general, the finer the state of sub-division of the material and therefore the greater its surface area for a given weight, the greater is the reinforcing effect. Indeed, carbon blacks are often distinguished by their surface areas, a 15 acre black, for instance, having ultimate particles so tiny that 1 lb. of the black will have a total particle surface area of 15 acres. A tyre tread formulation is probably the most highly developed technical compound, and the reinforcement of rubber has been studied mainly in relation to the use of carbon black in compounds for this type of service. Those who wish to study reinforcement in greater detail are recommended to Dr. Parkinson's Monograph on the subject, noted in the references at the end of the chapter. Fig. 30 shows in graphical form the effect on the stress-strain properties of the addition of a variety of reinforcing fillers to a natural rubber base mix, the filler loading being chosen to show maximum reinforcement.

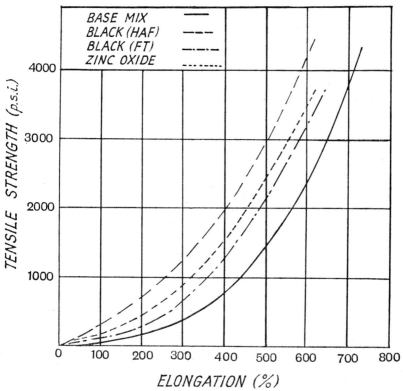

FIG. 30.   Stress-strain curves of reinforcing fillers in rubber.

Since the majority of fillers are much heavier than rubber, bulk for bulk, their addition gives weight to the compound. This added weight is rarely desirable and since it has considerable influence on the unit cost of the compound, we must discuss in some detail the question of rubber volume.

Density and Specific Gravity

The volume of a body is simply the amount of space it occupies, e.g. cubic inches, cubic centimetres, cubic feet, cubic miles. A cube is a regular solid with six square faces, the side of the cube which corresponds to the above cubic measurements being respectively one inch, one centimetre, one foot and one mile.

The density of a substance is simply the weight of unit volume of the substance, and it may be expressed in any unit of weight per any unit of volume (keeping British and metric systems separate), e.g. tons per cubic mile, pounds per cubic feet, cwts per cubic yard, grams per cubic centimetre, etc. When we wish to compare the densities of different substances, this method is somewhat cumbersome and a better way is to compare the density of the substance in question, with the density of a standard substance, i.e. to state its density relative to the standard substance. In the case of solids and liquids this standard is pure water.

The term 'relative density' is not much used nowadays, having been replaced by 'specific gravity'. The meaning is unaltered — it is the gravity (or 'weight') of a substance compared to the weight of an equal volume of a specific substance. The term 'specific gravity' is usually written as 'sp. gr.' or 'S.G.' and in the rubber industry is often shortened simply to 'gravity', a pardonable abbreviation so long as the users realise it is an abbreviation. The importance of specific gravity in rubber compounding is that, with very few exceptions, rubber products are not sold by weight but by size, which is just another way of saying by volume. Apart from flooring and tiling and some specialised applications, rubber compounds of high specific gravity are not desirable. For a given weight of rubber compound, a low specific gravity will give a greater volume than a high specific gravity and the low gravity mix will thus 'go further'. The consideration of compound volume rather than weight is a very important one — it is employed in compound design and costing, in calculating the correct weight to fill an internal mixer of given capacity, in calculating weights of 'blanks' for moulded products and in many other ways. If we know the compound formula — the kinds, amounts and specific gravities of the rubber and other compounding ingredients, it is quite simple to calculate the specific gravity of the compound. The method of making this calculation and other useful calculations relating to volume will be given in Appendix A. Meantime, to drive home the importance of this property here is a typical practical example. The fitment of a new wearing surface (or tread) to a worn tyre is a sound technical proposition and most tyre manufacturers sell to those firms who carry out this retreading operation, uncured rubber compound similar to that used for the treads of new tyres. This 'tread rubber' is extruded in a large variety of cross-sectional shapes to suit different sizes and types of tyre and different retreading equipment. The retreader buys this in coils of approximately 50 lb. weight, for which he pays a certain price per pound. The rubber strip is cut into lengths corresponding to the circumference of the particular tyre — a 50 lb. coil may give 10 treads each weighing 5 lb. If we assume that one compound (A) has a specific gravity of 1·00 and another tread rubber compound (B) has a specific gravity of double this figure, it should be obvious that each foot length of B will be twice as heavy as a foot length of A. The retreader will find that compound B will give him only 5 treads for the same weight of 50 lb. The specific gravity figures quoted are quite unrealistic — compounds for such tread rubber may vary from 1·10 to 1·20 depending on quality — but the principle is illustrated very effectively, the lower the specific gravity the more volume the customer gets for his money. Unless there are good reasons to the contrary the specific gravity of a rubber compound should be kept as low as possible provided the service requirements can be satisfied.

(a) Reinforcing fillers. (i) black

The most important reinforcing filler is carbon black, formerly produced mainly in the U.S.A. from natural gas, by the 'channel' process. The more efficient 'furnace' process is superseding the channel method, and natural gas as the raw material is giving way to oil residues. The production of carbon black need therefore no longer be located near a plentiful supply of natural gas and plants have now been set up in the U.K. for the manufacture of furnace black in quantities sufficient to cover practically all home needs. It should be remembered, however, that limited quantities of two types of furnace black of U.K. manufacture have been available for many years.

In the channel process small fan-shaped smoky flames, produced by burning natural gas in a limited supply of air, are allowed to play (or 'impinge') on the underside of reciprocating iron channels on which the black is deposited and then removed by scraping. The product is called gas black, channel black or impingement black. The yield is low, being only some 2 lb. per cu. ft. of gas, equivalent to about 3% of the available carbon.

In the furnace process, partial combustion of natural gas or oil residues takes place in large furnaces resulting in the production of carbon black and gaseous products. After cooling with water sprays the black is separated out by means of high voltage electrical pre-cipitators, followed by a battery of cyclone collectors. The yield of black from this process is equal to 36% of the available carbon, much higher than the yield from the channel method.

In the thermal decomposition process natural gas or atomised oil is decomposed by heat in a large furnace. The black is cooled by water spray and separated from the gaseous products by a bag filter system or by cyclone separators. The process is termed 'cyclic', two furnaces being worked as one production unit. As one furnace is being heated up to a temperature sufficiently high to 'crack' the gas, the other fur-nace is producing black. The first furnace then produces black while the second is being pre-heated. The product is termed 'thermal' black. The cyclic furnace method of manufacture was developed many years before the continuous furnace method.

These three methods are shown in diagrammatic form in Fig. 31.

Lamp black is another type of carbon black with a reinforcing power much inferior to that of either channel or furnace blacks. It is produced by burning oils in open pans, the product being collected in a cooling chamber.

When selecting a carbon black for reinforcing rubber, two main considerations must be borne in mind, firstly, its influence on the properties of the compound and, secondly, the adaptability of the black to the processing conditions existing in the factory. Although it is not the only factor of importance, generally speaking the reinforcing effect of carbon black increases as the size of the tiny particles decreases. Unfortunately, processing difficulties are found to increase with reduction in particle size — proper dispersion becomes less easy to achieve and there is a greater tendency to scorchiness.

A useful summary of the properties of carbon black in rubber in relation to particle size is given in Table V.

Table V

PARTICLE SIZE DECREASING

———————————————————————→

Easy processing	Hard processing
High resilience	Low resilience
Low abrasion resistance	High abrasion resistance
Low tensile strength	High tensile strength
Low heat generation	High heat generation

Prior to World War II the range of carbon blacks in bulk pro-duction for the reinforcement of rubber was limited to three types of

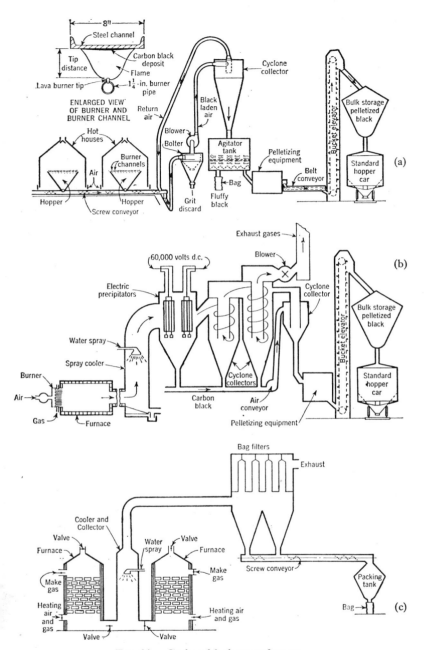

FIG. 31. Carbon black manufacture.

(a) Channel process; (b) Furnace combustion process;
(c) Furnace thermal process.

channel, one of furnace and two thermal blacks. There were a few others available but they were not produced in any great volume. The marketing of natural gas in the U.S.A. as a gaseous fuel, instead of using it for black production, and the advent of GR-S type synthetic rubber both stimulated the higher-yielding furnace process. Technique has improved so much that there is now a wide range of furnace blacks with reinforcing properties surpassing those of channel blacks. One of the reasons for this is that the particle size of a black depends on the time the small carbon particles are allowed to grow in the hot atmosphere. In the channel method only small variations in this time are possible, but conditions may be varied much more easily in the furnace process.

Carbon blacks are made by a large number of firms each using their own trade name, but the various types are represented by accepted abbreviations denoting their processing characteristics and method of manufacture, e.g. EPC denotes easy processing channel.

The following table gives the types of black in most common use, the fuel used and the approximate particle size in millimicrons. 1 millimicron (mμ) is equal to one-millionth of a millimetre.

Type	Name	Approx. particle size (mμ)	Fuel
EPC	Easy processing channel	30	Gas
MPC	Medium processing channel	25	Gas
SAF	Super abrasion furnace	25	Oil
ISAF	Intermediate super abrasion furnace	30	Oil
HAF	High abrasion furnace	45	Oil
FEF	Fast extrusion furnace	80	Oil
FF	Fine furnace	40	Gas
GPF	General purpose furnace	100	Oil-gas
HMF	High modulus furnace	95	Gas
SRF	Semi-reinforcing furnace	160	Gas
FT	Fine thermal	200	Gas
MT	Medium thermal	400	Gas

The specific gravity of all forms of carbon black is approximately 1·8.

Rubber is generally considered to be an excellent insulator but by the use of special types of black, it may be given a degree of electrical conductivity. Such conductive blacks have a very small particle size (10 to 15mμ). The conductivity is considered to be due to the building up of a network of chains with the particles touching each other. Conductive rubbers find many applications in situations where static electricity may build up due to friction, then discharge suddenly as a spark and ignite an inflammable gas or solvent. The conductivity of the rubber prevents such a dangerous accumulation, by permitting the static to leak to earth as it is formed.

Carbon black is a very dirty material to handle and over the years the manufacturers have made strenuous efforts to improve this aspect by either compressing, densifying or pelletising their product. Most blacks are now available in pelletised form, the free flowing properties of which lend themselves to bulk handling. The latest development is to add the carbon black to the latex during the manufacture of synthetic rubber and there are now on the market several SBR-carbon black masterbatches containing different types and proportions of black to suit various compound formulations. The advantages of buying carbon black in this way are obvious.

(a) Reinforcing fillers. (ii) non-black

In general, white or light-coloured products do not need the degree of reinforcement demanded by a tyre tread or conveyor belt cover. Consequently less attention has been paid to developing reinforcing fillers for such articles. Within the last ten years or so, however, the work on non-black fillers, particularly those based on the element silicon, has been intensified and has culminated in the proposed marketing of coloured tyres, the treads of which are claimed to wear as well as those made of compounds reinforced with carbon black. The introduction of synthetic rubber had some effect on this work since, unlike natural rubber, most synthetics have very poor physical properties unless considerable amounts of reinforcing fillers are added — in other words, the 'pure gum' properties of synthetics are much inferior to those of natural rubber.

The most important non-black fillers are zinc oxide, 'activated' whitings, some types of clay, magnesium carbonate and the silicon compounds — silicon dioxide, calcium silicate and aluminium silicate.

Zinc oxide (sp. gr. 5·57) is used as an accelerator activator, as noted in Chapter IX, as well as a white reinforcing filler. It is manufactured by two methods, the French or 'indirect' process and the American or 'direct' process. In the French process the oxide is made by combustion of metallic zinc which has previously been recovered from ore in a separate furnace. In the American process the zinc ore and coal are loaded together into a single furnace. The coal provides the heat for smelting and combines with the other components of the ore, thus freeing the zinc as vapour, which is then burned in air to form zinc oxide. Lead is often found in association with zinc ores and, if it remains as an impurity in the finished zinc oxide in any but the smallest percentages, darkening of a light-coloured article may result. This is because lead combines with the sulphur, used for vulcanisation, forming lead sulphide. This compound is black in colour, and so darkens white or light-coloured articles.

Ordinary whiting, chemically calcium carbonate (sp. gr. approx. 2·65) is a popular extending filler, but if it is specially treated so that each particle is coated with stearic acid or a similar fatty acid it has good reinforcing properties. Generally, such 'activated' whitings, of which there are a variety on the market under several trade names, are based on calcium carbonate produced by a chemical process and called 'precipitated' whiting. Precipitation is the name given to the formation of a mass of fine particles in a solution as a result of a chemical reaction. Particle size is of importance in the reinforcing effect of whitings, as it is with all fillers. The comparatively large particles (30–40 microns) of dry ground limestone, which is a form of naturally-occurring calcium carbonate, have little or no reinforcing value, while the ultra-fine precipitated whitings at the other end of the scale have quite a considerable reinforcing effect.

The term clay is applied to a wide variety of materials, which are known chemically as hydrated aluminium silicates. The rubber industry is interested mainly in china clay (kaolin) and in bentonite clay. Kaolin has a moderate reinforcing effect but the bentonite variety, treated or 'activated' with certain organic chemicals known as amines, can produce tensile strengths equal to those given by an MPC carbon black. Rubber clays are often termed 'hard' or 'soft', but this does not refer to the clays themselves but to their effect on the properties imparted to a rubber compound. Extensive deposits of clay are found in the U.S.A. and in Devon and Cornwall in the U.K. where the clay is obtained by mining. No deep tunnelling is involved, the process being more like open-cast working. The over-burden is removed and the clay washed down by high pressure hoses to the lowest level of the pit. Foreign matter settles out, after which the clay stream is pumped to the top level for further settling and refining. The cream-like slurry is partly dried out by a filter press and, for use in rubber, the clay is further dried in a kiln to reduce the moisture content to approximately 1%. The specific gravity of rubber clay is about 2·60.

The variety of magnesium carbonate (sp. gr. 2·20 approx.) used in rubber compounding is mainly the precipitated type, which has a greater reinforcing power than the product prepared from the naturally occurring mineral, magnesite.

Silica (sp. gr. 2·00 approx.) is chemically silicon dioxide and is produced by either combustion or precipitation. In the first method a mixture of hydrogen and silicon tetrachloride is burned under a slowly revolving drum. The silicon dioxide which is deposited on the drum is scraped off and removed by conveyor. The process is thus similar to one of the methods of making carbon black and, since it has reinforcing powers akin to those of carbon black, this silicon product has been called 'white carbon'. The precipitated product is made by treatment of a solution of a soluble silicate.

Calcium silicate (sp. gr. 2·10) and aluminium silicate (sp. gr. 2·60) are both prepared by a precipitation process.

Compounding with silica and silicates is a little tricky, since some types have a retarding effect on cure but may be scorchy during mixing. As always, the manufacturers will supply full compounding information on their products; two papers on the subject are noted in the references at the end of the chapter.

(b) Extending Fillers

In the early days of rubber compounding a truly astonishing variety of materials was proposed and used for addition to rubber with the object of making it 'go further'. During World War II, of course, because of the shortage of the normal ingredients, some rather unusual extending fillers were used. Here however we will only mention those in common use at the present time. These are ordinary (i.e. not activated) whitings and clays, barytes (ba-rī′-tēz), talc, factice and vulcanised rubber crumb.

The whitings used as extending fillers are obtained by fine grinding of either limestone or chalk, both of which are different forms of naturally-occurring calcium carbonate.

Clays of large particle size, and therefore cheap, are used in rubber as extending fillers. Clays of very small particle size ('colloidal' clays) and treated clays have already been mentioned.

Barytes is chemically barium sulphate, the mineral being ground down to suitable particle size for use in rubber. The precipitated form of barium sulphate is known as blanc fixe. Both are used as extending fillers especially where, as in chemical plant lining, the product has to be resistant to acids and alkalis. Barium sulphate has a high specific gravity (ground barytes 4·45, blanc fixe 4·20) and is a useful filler in those cases where weight is desired in a compound.

Talc (sp. gr. 2·72) is a naturally-occurring mineral of which there are many varieties, other names being soapstone and french chalk. The latter variety should not be confused with chalk itself which is calcium carbonate. Talc is best known in many factories as a dusting agent which prevents the sticky surfaces of unvulcanised rubber from adhering, but it is a popular filler in cable compounds.

A useful extending filler is rubber substitute (often abbreviated in the factory simply to 'sub') but now generally known as factice (fak'-tis). It is included in this section for convenience although many would consider it more as a processing aid. Factice is a rubbery material made by 'vulcanising' certain vegetable oils, usually rapeseed oil. Dark factice is obtained by heating the oil with sulphur, white factice by treating the oil with sulphur chloride. Suitable types of factice are now available for use in most synthetic rubbers. The specific gravity of factice varies with the particular type and ranges from 1·02 to 1·08, i.e. it is not much heavier than water. Factice is therefore employed where a 'floating' compound is required, that is a product which will float in water.

Mineral rubber (sp. gr. approx. 1·04) is not now 'mineral' and never was 'rubber'. It is a bituminous material produced by blowing air through molten bitumen. In small proportions it is really a tack-producing softener, but in larger amounts can be classed as an extender. It is often referred to as MRX. There are many varieties, distinguished by their melting points.

An extending filler may of course be called an 'extender', but this term is nowadays reserved more for certain residues obtained as by-products in the refining of petroleum. These could also be classed, when used in smaller proportions, as processing aids and softeners.

Vulcanised rubber in any form (moulding spue, reject or worn out products) may be ground down on a rubber mill with a tight nip or in a special crumb-grinding mill to produce a useful extending filler. The physical properties do not become poorer in proportion to the percentage of crumb added and it is common practice to use quite large amounts in articles in which the service requirements do not call for the utmost in flex life, resistance to abrasion, etc.

GROUP 7. SOFTENERS

The functions of this class of compounding ingredients depend somewhat on the amount added, in small quantities of say 2 to 5 PHR they facilitate mixing, especially in heavily loaded compounds, and assist in processing. Rather larger amounts may be added with the object of softening the 'vulcanisate' — another name for the product of vulcanisation when we are not specifying any particular shape or form. In very large amounts, say 50 to 100 PHR, we have already met some 'softeners' in their role as extenders. This group illustrates very well the dual function of some compounding ingredients as was mentioned in Chapter IX; some softeners increase the tack of the unvulcanised compound as well as softening it; others restrain the blooming of sulphur; stearic acid, already discussed as an accelerator activator, aids in the dispersion of fillers; and so on. Softeners act mainly by mere physical lubrication of the rubber molecules and a clear distinction must be made between softeners and peptising agents, which have been called 'chemical softeners'. Peptisers act chemically on the rubber molecules and such small quantities are needed that their effect on the properties of the vulcanisate is negligible. However, although it depends on the amount added, the effect of the softeners is carried through to the vulcanisate.

Once the correct balance has been found for the sulphur/accelerator/activator complex, the compounder must next apply his skill to the choice of the softener. It must be the most suitable type and in the right amount to meet both the requirements of processing and the service requirements of the product. The choice is not easy and experience of the particular product and of the factory equipment is essential. Here is an outline of the softeners in common use.

Stearic and oleic acids, in addition to their use as softeners, are favoured because they assist the dispersion of fillers and act as accelerator activators.

Pine tar is the best-known tack producer or tackifier. Gum and wood rosins, coumarone resins and rosin oils may also be used to enhance this property. The satisfactory adhesion of unvulcanised components depends on this property, and it is of course also important in compounds used for frictioning fabrics. Many oils prepared from petroleum have excellent softening properties, petroleum jelly itself being popular in sponge mixes. Paraffin wax assists processing, particularly extrusion, but may bloom to the surface and reduce building tack.

Petroleum oils, factice and mineral rubber have already been mentioned when we were discussing extenders.

Most softeners have specific gravities in the range 0·90 to 1·05 and, except in very special cases, there is no need to worry about the added weight which they give to a rubber compound.

GROUP 8. PROTECTIVE AGENTS

Rubber products are subjected to a variety of deteriorating influences mainly during their service life, although the time they spend in storage before use (shelf-life) must also be considered. Deterioration in a product is largely the result of oxidation, which means that the rubber molecules are attacked and oxidised by atmospheric oxygen or the more active ozone. This attack is accelerated by heat, light and exposure to oils and solvents. The compounder is not nowadays limited to natural rubber as his only elastomer and, when he knows the conditions to which the product will be subjected he can select the best synthetic elastomers — neoprene for weather resistance, nitrile rubber for oil and solvent resistance, silicone rubber for resistance to extremely high temperatures, etc. Although some degree of protection may be obtained by spraying or painting the product with a protective substance, this has limited application and it is customary to add a protective agent to the rubber at the mixing stage. Such materials are termed, in general, 'antioxidants', although varieties specially designed to resist attack by ozone have been marketed in recent years as 'antiozonants'. Typical of such antioxidants, all of which are complex organic substances, is phenyl-beta-naphthylamine, which is usually abbreviated to PBN, or sometimes PBNA.

Those antioxidants which show the maximum protection are found to cause darkening (or staining) of white and light-coloured articles, but 'non-staining' varieties are available in which this effect has been reduced to a minimum. Cracking due to mechanical working (flex cracking) is reduced by the addition to the compound of yet another variety, an anti-flex-cracking antioxidant.

The action of antioxidants and antiozonants is a chemical one, but protection can be obtained by physical means. This is achieved by the addition to the compound of a substance which will bloom continuously to the surface of the product, and thus form a protective film. Paraffin wax itself and waxes with a very fine crystalline structure (micro-crystalline waxes) are typical of this class of protective agent.

In the United Kingdom, students will be most familiar with the series of antioxidants sold by Imperial Chemical Industries under the trade name 'Nonox', the 'Agerite' series marketed by R. T. Vanderbilt Co. Inc., and the 'Santoflex' products of Monsanto Chemicals Ltd.

Antioxidants are used in quite small amounts (0·5 to 1 PHR) except where the service conditions are extremely severe.

GROUP 9. SPECIAL COMPONENTS

(a) Blowing Agents

Although latex foam has superseded sponge rubber to a very large extent, some applications still require sponge made in the traditional manner. Sponge rubber is made by incorporating in the rubber compound materials capable of generating large volumes of gas, when heated in the normal course of vulcanisation. The blowing agents originally used were sodium bicarbonate (baking soda) and ammonium bicarbonate, which both produce carbon dioxide on heating, but these have been replaced to some extent by a number of organic chemicals which give off nitrogen when heated.

In the production of moulded hollow balls, the inflation gas is produced by the decomposition of tablets of ammonium chloride and sodium nitrite.

(b) Abrasives

In rubber erasers and grinding wheels the abrasive effect is achieved by mixing into the rubber compound such materials as coarse silica and ground pumice stone.

(c) Colours

The public have tended to associate red with high quality in a rubber product. Indeed, in some Asiatic territories it is impossible to sell inner tubes in any other colour, despite the superior service given by tube compounds reinforced with carbon black. The reason for the public acceptance of red rubber, which technically is quite unjustifiable, is that one of the earliest vulcanising agents, antimony trisulphide, imparted a reddish colour to the compound.

With the exception of red iron oxide, most inorganic colouring materials for rubber have been replaced by organic substances, now

I   C.R.T.

that some of the early defects in the latter have been overcome, e.g. instability when subjected to heat during vulcanisation (particularly in open steam) and 'bleeding', which is the migration of one colour into an adjacent colour in multi-coloured articles.

We must mention some inorganic materials which are used either to make a white-coloured rubber or to act as a background for other colours. Titanium dioxide (sp. gr. 4·0 approx.) is the finest white pigment known, but it is very expensive and a cheaper modification, namely titanium dioxide on a barium sulphate base, is often used instead. Zinc oxide, which we have met both as an activator and as a white reinforcing filler, is also an excellent white pigment. Lithopone (sp. gr. 4·2 approx.) is a mixture of about 30% zinc sulphide and 70% barium sulphate, precipitated together.

When a pure white is required it is customary to add a trace of a blue pigment to the compound in order to counteract any tendency towards 'yellowing' which might occur during vulcanisation or in service.

(d) Retarders

With correct balancing of the curatives in a rubber compound, it should be unnecessary to add a material which restrains or retards the vulcanisation reaction. However in difficult cases, e.g. the use of scorchy furnace blacks, their use may be advisable. Retarders are complex organic substances, a popular one being acetyl salicylic acid, better known as the humble aspirin.

(e) Dusting and Anti-tack Agents

When sheets of unvulcanised rubber are to be temporarily piled one on top of the other or otherwise brought in contact, the surfaces must be treated with an anti-tack agent, in order to ensure easy subsequent separation. When used in dry powder form such materials are, in the factory, collectively termed 'chalk', an abbreviation of french chalk, also known as talc or soapstone (chalk itself is calcium carbonate). Such powders may be used as suspensions in water, which reduces the contamination of the atmosphere and makes for healthier working conditions. When chalked slabs of mixed rubber compound are remilled prior to calendering or extrusion, the dusting agent will unavoidably be incorporated in the rubber. When a consequent lowering of the physical properties of the product is undesirable, clay may be substituted for talc as the dusting agent.

When assembling an article from a number of 'chalked' components, it is of course necessary to remove all traces of the dusting agent from the areas to be bonded together. In processes in which there is no opportunity for cleaning off the dusting agent, the material to use is zinc stearate which dissolves in the rubber at curing temperatures and does not impair knitting of the components. It follows that the most careful control should be exercised over the issue of 'chalk' and zinc stearate since confusion in their use may have disastrous consequences.

(f) Latex Chemicals

The manufacture of articles direct from liquid latex, e.g. latex foam, dipped goods, adhesives, etc. is a branch of the industry with a technology of its own. Although the principles of compounding are the same as for dry rubber manufacture, all ingredients for addition to latex must be in the form of water dispersions. This mode of manufacture thus adds to our already long list of compounding ingredients a host of substances — wetting and dispersing agents, stabilisers, foaming agents, and coagulants, the uses of which will be outlined when 'Latex Manufacture' is discussed.

In the space at our disposal it has been possible only to give an introduction to compounding ingredients and their uses. It will suffice for the student of general rubber technology, but those intending to specialise as compounders should have access to References 1 and 2 and should study very closely Dr. Flint's article, Reference 3.

REFERENCES

WILSON, B. J., *British Compounding Ingredients*. Cambridge.

Vanderbilt Rubber Handbook. 1948 or 1958, New York, U.S.A.

FLINT, C. F., The Economics of Factice in Rubber Compounding: A Note for Students. *Rubber Journal*. 1955, Vol. 129, 558

POWELL, L. S., *Elementary Physics for Technical Students*, Chap. II, London

PARKINSON, D., *Reinforcement of Rubber*. Institution of the Rubber Industry, London

MOAKES, R. C. W. and PYNE, J. R., White Reinforcing Fillers in Natural Rubber and High Styrene Copolymers. *Proc. Inst. Rubber Ind.*, 1954, Vol. 1, 151

HARRIS, J. D., Compounding with New Silica and Silicate Fillers. *Proc. Inst. Rubber Ind.*, 1956, Vol. 3, 145

Carbon Black, an RPW Special Feature. *Rubb. Plast. Weekly*, 1962, Vol. 142, 280

CHAPTER XI

TEXTILES IN THE RUBBER INDUSTRY

Since it has been estimated that some 80% of all rubber consumed, is used in association with a textile material, training in rubber technology must include the rudiments of textile technology. Those who wish to specialise in one of the branches of the rubber industry which makes extensive use of textiles (tyres, footwear, belting, hose, etc.) would be well advised to take a short course specially arranged to meet the requirements of buyers, salesmen, yarn and cloth merchants, and others who wish an introduction to the subject. Such courses are run as evening classes in the technical colleges of most large towns during the winter session. Attendance at a course of this nature will enable the rubber technician who has to deal with fabrics to talk to his textile counterpart in the language of the textile industry, the jargon of which is just as colourful as is that of the rubber industry.

In addition to those textiles which become part of the product, the rubber industry uses a vast amount of woven fabric, generally termed industrial processing cloths. These are linings (or 'liners') for the storage of unvulcanised sheet rubber and of coated fabrics. Such linings may be given a surface treatment to reduce the tendency for the tacky rubber to adhere to the textile, thus facilitating removal, without distortion, of the rubber or coated fabric. Other unvulcanised components such as tyre treads may be stored in 'books', the leaves of which are made of lining material. Some of the other ancillary uses of textiles in the rubber industry are wrappers or 'leaders' in the proofing operation, wrapping tapes and cloths for use in the open steam vulcanisation process and gauze bags for 'dusting' rubber surfaces (the controlled application of anti-tack agents, such as soapstone and zinc stearate, to unvulcanised rubber sheet). In supplying unvulcanised rubber sheet and rubbered fabrics for the repair of tyres, inner tubes, belting and hose, extensive use was once made of 'holland cloth' (also known as glazed linen) which is a thin sheeting filled with a starchy material giving it a glossy non-adherent surface. However holland cloth has now been almost entirely superseded by thin films of polythene, one of the large class of high polymers known collectively as 'plastics'.

The dictionary defines the word 'textile' as 'a material suitable for weaving' or 'a woven fabric'. We might amplify this bare definition to (a) a fibrous material suitable for spinning and making into a yarn, and (b) an assembly of interlacing yarns or fibres in the form of woven, knitted or other structures. In the rubber industry the term 'textile' is widened to include any material used for the structural reinforcement of a product and thus includes such materials as steel and glass, not normally classed as textiles.

We have not yet explained just why many products made from our versatile raw material require textile reinforcement. Briefly, the combination of textile and rubber suppresses the high extensibility of the rubber and permits the full strength of the textile to be realised. The necessity for the use of rubber/textile composites should be clear when we remember that the best compounded rubbers break at a load of about 4,000 p.s.i., compared to a breaking load of some 100,000 p.s.i. for textile fibres. When we consider relative elongations, how-ever, the opposite is true, textile fibres breaking at about 10% stretch, whereas the rubber may show an elongation of about 600% at breaking point. The rubber also insulates the textile yarns, fibres and plies and prevents early failure of the product in service.

In this chapter we must of necessity confine our remarks to those textiles used extensively in the rubber industry, although others may be mentioned by way of illustrating a particular point. We will discuss materials, forms and structures, and finally compare those properties of the textiles which have a bearing on their use in rubber/textile composites.

Materials

Textile materials are obtained

(a) from natural sources, either animal, vegetable or mineral;
(b) by a modification of a substance already found in nature;
(c) by synthesis of fibre-forming polymers.

A distinction must be made between group (b) to which the name 'man-made' has been applied and group (c) the truly synthetic materials. The best-known man-made fibre is rayon in which naturally-occurring cellulose (the cell walls of plants) is modified or 'regenerated' to make a textile. Nylon and Terylene are examples of group (c); they are products of chemical interaction and are quite unknown in nature.

Table VI summarises those textiles of interest to the rubber industry.

(a) Natural — Animal   — wool and silk
                Vegetable — cotton and flax (linen)
                Mineral   — asbestos and glass
(b) Man-made   rayon
(c) Synthetic   nylon and Terylene

Note that rayon and nylon which have now become generic terms for a class of fibres are spelt with small initial letters; Terylene (named Dacron in the U.S.A.) requires a capital letter since it is still a trade-name; it should also be noted that, although there are three chemical variations of rayon, we are interested only in that type known as viscose rayon.

Forms

All the natural fibres with the exception of silk are obtained originally in the form of fibres, which are quite short in the case of cotton ($\frac{1}{2}$ in. to 2 in.) but considerably longer for wool (2 in. to 12 in.). In general the longer the fibre the better is its quality. The term used to describe collectively the fibres of a textile is 'staple', but when we speak of the staple of a single fibre it denotes its length. Silk is extruded by the silk-worm in long continuous lengths. Fibres occurring in this form are usually termed 'filaments'.

Man-made and synthetic textiles are manufactured in continuous filament form and largely, of course they are used in this form. For some purposes the continuous filament may be cut up into staple fibres and spun into a yarn. One reason for this apparently uneconomic process is that man-made and synthetic fibres have a smooth polished surface, which is without the 'hairiness' of natural fibres, and this results in poor adhesion to rubber. When such continuous filament material is used in a textile/rubber composite, it is necessary to treat the surface of the textile with special 'dopes' to promote adhesion. This is done by passing the textile through a bath, containing either a preparation of latex-resorcinol-formaldehyde (LRF) or of an isocyanate — a chemical substance which reacts with both the textile fibre and the rubber. LRF dopes are generally used for rayon, isocyanates for nylon and Terylene.

Structures

Staple fibres are twisted together (or 'spun') to produce yarns and several of these single yarns may again be twisted together, depending on the qualities desired in the finished structure. Continuous filaments may also be twisted together if desired.

In order to illustrate this 'folding' process, we will describe the make-up of typical cotton and rayon cords for the manufacture of the textile reinforcement of pneumatic tyres. We will also introduce the systems of denoting yarn thicknesses, which we refer to as the 'count' of a yarn. Cotton in pneumatic tyres has been almost entirely superseded by rayon and nylon; however, a typical cotton cord had the construction denoted by the code 23ˢ/5/3, which indicates that 5 single yarns each of 23ˢ count were twisted together to form a thread, and 3 of these threads were combined to form the cord. The count of a yarn is the number of times a standard length is contained in 1 lb. The standard length (termed hank, skein or cut) varies for different materials and the standard lengths of a single material may also vary in different districts. The situation is therefore rather confusing. For cotton the length of hank is 840 yd. The higher the count number the greater is the length making up a weight of 1 lb. and therefore the thinner the yarn; this 'count' system is thus an 'indirect' system.

A popular rayon cord has the construction 2/1650 denier (sometimes written 1650/2) which indicates that 2 yarns consisting of a large number of continuous filaments totalling 1650 denier are twisted together to form the cord. The thickness of man-made and synthetic fibres is denoted by the 'denier', a number which gives the weight in grams of 9,000 metres of yarn. Each single yarn of the above rayon cord thus has a weight of 1,650 gm. for a length of 9,000 m. It follows that the thinner the filament the smaller the denier number; as the number increases so does the thickness of the yarn. This system of numbering yarns is thus a 'direct' system. Conversion of indirect counts to the direct denier system is a simple arithmetical calculation. However, the advantages of a universal yarn numbering system are obvious and several have been proposed in recent years. A number denoting the weight in grams for a length of 10,000 m. of yarn has received some acceptance, but it will be many years before the old systems are superseded.

The expressions 23ˢ/5/3 and 2/1650 described the single cotton and rayon cords respectively. For use as tyre fabric these are woven into structures with a number of cords per inch of width, depending on the particular part of the tyre carcass in which it is to be employed. For very large scale tyre manufacture the fabric need not be woven. The cords, suitably spaced, are passed directly to the calender, where they receive a coating of rubber which holds them in the correct relative positions.

The strength of yarns, threads or cords may be expressed as the load in pounds required to break them, but for ease of comparison it is much more convenient to state their 'tenacity'. This is the breaking load expressed in grams per denier of the yarn, e.g. a 2/1650 denier cord breaking at a load of 30 lb. would have a tenacity of just over 4 gm./denier.

Fabric structures may be either felted, knitted, lace, woven or bonded. Felted fabrics are made by beating together the individual fibres, which then adhere by their own hairiness. Knitted and lace fabrics are formed by making a series of interlaced loops. Bonded fabrics (sometimes termed 'non-woven') are becoming of increasing importance because their manufacture is economical; they are made by positioning the fibres and cementing them in the pre-formed arrangement with a suitable bonding agent, such as rubber latex.

Woven fabrics are composed of threads running longitudinally (lengthwise along the fabric) and threads running transversely (crosswise), which in the weaving process are interlaced with each other according to the desired structure and design. The lengthwise threads are collectively called the 'warp' and individual warp threads are termed 'ends'. The crosswise threads are the 'weft' and individual weft threads are termed 'picks', 'shots' or 'filling threads'. We have already met the word 'count' in relation to yarn numbering; the same word is used to denote the number of threads per inch used in constructing the cloth. Warp count is the number of ends per inch of width of the cloth and weft count is the number of picks per inch of length. A cloth count is written simply as, say, 24×22, the first number referring to the ends and the second to the picks.

The ends and picks may be composed of any of the materials already mentioned, the yarns being given a twist of a certain number of turns per inch in the direction demanded by the properties required in the finished fabric. Twist is coded S or Z, depending on whether the direction of the yarn runs downwards from left to right as in the central part of the letter S or upwards from left to right as in the central bar of the letter Z. The threads may be singles yarn, 2/fold,

3/fold, etc., and the relative strength of warp to weft is suited to the product in which the textile is to be incorporated. Tyre cord has all its strength in the warp, the weft being present only to hold the warp in position until the cord is rubbered. In belting duck the warp is

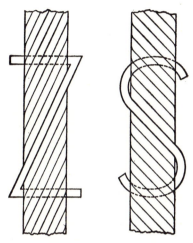

FIG. 32.   Z and S twists

stronger than the weft, since it is the warp which takes most of the stresses in service. Hose duck is used on the bias and therefore warp and weft are equal in strength.

The Weaving Process

Woven fabrics are made on an intricate machine called a 'loom'. Looms are to be found in many sizes and types depending on the quality of fabric being woven. The spun yarn, which will constitute the warp, is transferred from the spinning bobbins to a cone which may hold many miles of thread. The weft yarn is wound directly on to a 'pirn', a slender bobbin, fitting inside the shuttle. The cones of warp yarn are placed in a large frame called a 'creel' and the threads led through a comb-like spacing device, in the correct sequence. To get the large number of yarns required by the width of the warp, several 'back beams' are assembled behind a 'slashing frame', which gives the yarns a coat of size to protect them during the weaving process. The warp beams are raised and lowered in a sequence which is determined by the design of the fabric being woven — plain weave, satin weave or twill weave, or any variant on these basic weaves. The action of the warp beams causes the rows of warp yarn to diverge in V-formation, the opening so formed being termed a 'shed'. The shuttle, holding its pirn of weft and trailing the yarn behind it, flies across the shed at high speed and lays down the weft thread between the warp yarns. Another comb-like device, the 'reed', beats the weft firmly up to the woven cloth, the beams then change over the shed and the shuttle returns across it, laying down another weft thread.

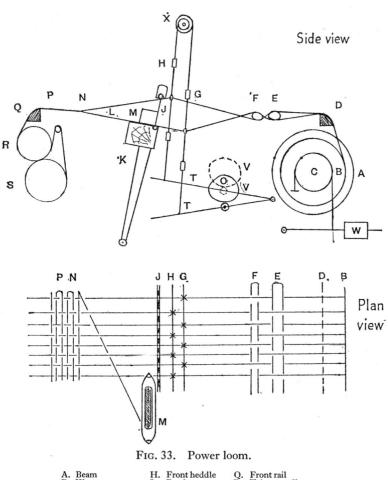

FIG. 33.   Power loom.

A. Beam	H. Front heddle	Q. Front rail
B. Warp yarn	J. Reed	R. Take-up roller
C. Collar	K. Sley	S. Cloth roller
D. Back rail	L. Shed	T. Treadles
E. Back lease rod	M. Shuttle	V. Tappets
F. Front lease rod	N. Fell	W. Weighting system
G. Back heddle	P. Cloth	X. Top roller mounting

The chief movements in weaving are therefore (*a*) shedding — moving the beams to form two lines of warp threads, (*b*) picking — throwing the shuttle through the shed and (*c*) beating up — pushing the weft by the reed up to the cloth already woven. The edge of the cloth, where the shuttle changes direction, is known as the selvedge, the line of which is thus parallel to the warp threads.

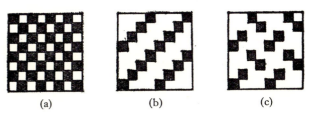

(a)   (b)   (c)

FIG. 34.   Types of weave.

(*a*) plain; (*b*) twill; (*c*) satin.

Fig. 33 shows a simple loom mounting. *A* is the warp beam, from which the warp threads pass over the back-rest *D* and through the eyes of the healds *G*, *H*. The required number of ends is passed through each split of the reed *J*. As the cloth *P* is woven, it is drawn over the breast beam *Q* by the roller *R* and passed to the cloth beam *S*. The weft is inserted in the shed *L*, by the shuttle *M*.

In a plain weave, Fig. 34 (*a*), the threads interlace in alternate order, no thread passes over more than one thread at a time in either direction and there is an intersection of adjacent threads at every possible point. In a satin weave, Fig. 34 (*c*), the warp threads may pass over several weft threads at a time, producing what is called a 'float'. In a five-end satin, for example, each end passes over four picks, then under one, and repeats this indefinitely. This gives a warp-faced fabric, the nature of the surface being determined mainly by the character of the yarns of which the warp is composed. In the proofing industry such weaves may be employed to improve the adhesion of rubber to fabric, e.g., a satin weave, with a warp of continuous fila-ment yarn, and a weft of spun staple yarn will produce a cloth with a warp face having the sheen of continuous filament and a weft face capable of good adhesion to rubber — the fibre ends projecting from the spun staple weft giving good anchorage for the rubber. A twill weave, Fig. 34 (*b*), is a decorative weave showing diagonal lines on the surface of the fabric. The twill lines are formed on both sides of the cloth and may run either to the left or right. The warp and weft floats on one side of the cloth correspond to weft and warp floats on the other.

Properties of Textile Materials

At this level of instruction we cannot discuss in detail the properties of textiles. In evaluating the suitability of a textile for a particular product, it is important to consider the behaviour of the material under service conditions, e.g. some types of tyres and of conveyor belting may run at quite high temperatures, others may operate under cold, wet conditions. There are fundamental differences between the textiles we have mentioned — cotton, rayon, nylon, Terylene, glass and steel — but the textile technologist can make them all into suitable structures for use with rubber. The choice of one or the other may be based on price, availability, ease of manufacture, or even fashion and advertising, none of which are strictly the province of the rubber technician.

Table VII summarises the main properties of the more important textiles used in rubber/textile composites.

Property	Cotton	Viscose rayon	Modified rayon	Nylon	Terylene
Tenacity (gm./denier)	2·0–4·9	2·3–4·3	5·0–10·0	4·5–8·0	4·0–7·
Elongation at break (%)	3–7	9–20	6	19–30	11–3(
Specific Gravity	1·53	1·52	1·50	1·14	1·38
Moisture absorption %, at 95% rel. humidity	24–27	27	20	8	0·5
Effect of heat	Decomposes at 300° F	Decomposes at 350–400° F	Similar to cotton	Melts at 480° F	Melts at 480°

REFERENCES

The Textile Students Manual. London
HARTLEY, T. R., Tyre Cords. Proc. Inst. Rubber Ind. 1956, Vol. 3, 76
BOWDEN, W. and WILSON, A. J., Natural and Synthetic Polymers in Conveyor Belting. Proc. Inst. Rubber Ind. 1958, Vol. 5, 129

FIG. 35. Weaving belting duck.

CHAPTER XII

THE MANUFACTURE OF RUBBER PRODUCTS

This chapter covers the manufacture of a great many diverse products. Rubber used for transportation, mainly as pneumatic tyres, accounts for considerably more than half of all rubber production, and will therefore be discussed at some length. It should be remembered, however, that, in its own way, the small factory which can at short notice turn out an intricate gasket for, say, an urgent ship repair job, is just as important as the large unit producing tyres to a schedule planned for several months ahead. We will make some mention of the branches of the industry which produce goods other than tyres, although a complete coverage of all rubber products would require several volumes.

The student should supplement the information given here by taking full advantage of factory visits and film shows arranged by his instructors. In attempting to answer an examination question on manufacture he would be wise to select, if at all possible, a branch of the industry with which he is well acquainted.

PNEUMATIC TYRES

For convenience we will deal with this section under the headings — Evolution, Duties, Construction, Development and Manufacture.

Evolution of the Tyre

Transporting himself and his goods and chattels from place to place has always been one of man's chief problems. The present-day wheel has evolved from the early tree trunks or round stones used simply as rollers, by way of the wooden wheel, which was fitted with an outer band of hard-wearing metal as soon as the practice of metal working became common. The name, tyre, derives from this function of the metal band in acting as a 'tier' (tying together the wooden parts of a wheel). The spelling 'tyre' appears less correct than the variation 'tire' which is common usage in the U.S.A., and in the publications of *The Times* Publishing Co. Ltd., London. There is some evidence, from excavations at Pompeii, that the Romans were using vehicles fitted with iron tyres, and since travelling in any type of vehicle fitted with a solid wheel was naturally most uncomfortable, many expedients were tried to give some degree of resilience to either the wheels or the vehicle. The ancient Egyptians made a springy floor for their vehicles by interlacing leather thongs. Much later, when the properties of metals were studied more closely, various types of springy metal wheels were designed and tried out but they did not prove successful. In times of rubber shortage, however, as in World War II, these designs have been re-examined and some degree of success has been reported.

With the advent of rubber, iron and steel tyres were replaced by solid rubber tyres on those vehicles in which their comfort, silence and speed would be most appreciated. The new material was first adopted for bicycles, hansom cabs and other horse-drawn carriages. The introduction of the 'pneumatic' principle — supporting the load of a vehicle on a cushion of air — by R. W. Thomson and J. B Dunlop in 1845 and 1888 respectively, has already been discussed in Chapter II. Thomson describes his invention as a "hollow belt composed of India Rubber or Gutta Percha and inflated with air to present a cushion of air to ground, rail or track". Dunlop claimed a "hollow tyre or tube of indiarubber and cloth or other suitable material, to contain air under pressure and to be attached to the wheel in such a method as may be found most suitable". From these modest statements has grown an industry, which can now supply pneumatic tyres for everything on wheels, from the humble barrow to the largest aeroplane. The original inventions of Thomson and Dunlop were single tube tyres, i.e. there was no separate outer cover and air-containing inner tube. These came later and were developed because of the difficulty of refitting the single tube tyre to the rims then available. It is extremely interesting to note that the outer cover and inner tube have recently been combined in the 'tubeless' tyre.

Duties of the Pneumatic Tyre

The pneumatic tyre has excellent shock-absorbing qualities and it distributes the weight of the vehicle over a substantial area of road surface. The payload of the vehicle is thus carried efficiently and with comfort. The tyre is the last link between engine and road, and its grip of the unyielding road surface very effectively converts the effort of the engine into movement of the vehicle. This efficient road grip is also important when the vehicle is required to accelerate, to change its direction, or to reduce its speed by the application of the brakes. The user expects that all these duties will be carried out without serious loss of efficiency throughout the entire life of the tyre, or more correctly throughout the life of the tread portion, since the fitment of a new tread to a sound casing is now an accepted part of tyre service. In view of the fact that many of the requirements of tyre design are somewhat contradictory, e.g. tread must be hard wearing, casing flexible and beads rigid, it is gratifying to know that tyre design has kept pace with modern car design, in which improved acceleration, better stability on cornering and increased maximum speeds all tend to reduce tyre life.

Construction of the Pneumatic Tyre

Although the modern pneumatic tyre may consist of as few as a dozen or as many as seventy-five single components, the general structure (shown in Fig. 36) may be considered as having three main

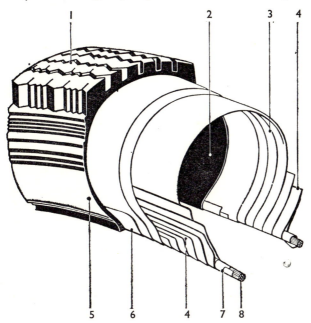

Fig. 36.   Structure of pneumatic tyre.

1, tread; 2, inner liner; 3, casing plies; 4, filler strips; 5, sidewall;
6, chafer; 7, bead wrapping; 8, bead wire.

features — the tread, the casing and the beads. The tread is that part of the tyre which grips the road; it has a characteristic pattern which varies according to different manufacturers' preferences, but which follows certain general trends according to the service for which the tyre is intended, e.g. General Purpose, Cross Country, Farm Tractor, etc. The tread rubber is compounded to be resistant to abrasion and cutting, and it should wear slowly and evenly. The casing itself is a strong yet flexible structure composed of a number of plies of cotton, rayon or nylon cord fabric, each cord being completely covered with a 'casing' type of rubber which separates it from its neighbours in the same ply and also from the cords in adjacent plies. This casing rubber, which is much softer than tread rubber, is compounded to provide good anchorage for the cords and to withstand the continual flexing of the casing during service. Most tyres are fitted with 'breaker' strips, plies of fabric of a more open construction than casing plies, thus giving a higher proportion of rubber to fabric than in the casing. Their function is to 'break' or spread the effect of impact shocks received by the tread. Depending on the size of tyre either one or two breakers may be fitted, but for some types of service they are found unnecessary and may be omitted. The cords of the casing and breaker plies run at an angle across the cover section, the size of this 'bias' angle being set by the tyre designer to give it the required combination of flexibility and stability. The bead assembly, strong steel wires insulated with rubber, holds the tyre on the rim and also provides an anchorage for the casing plies, thus enabling them to develop their full strength. Rubbered fabric chafer strips are fitted at the bead area to protect it from chafing by the metal of the rim.

It must be remembered that in the pneumatic tyre it is really air under pressure which carries the load of the vehicle, and the outer cover we have just described therefore has the further duty of protecting the inner tube which contains this compressed air. In the case of truck and bus tyres a strip of rubber (the 'flap') is fitted between the beads of the cover to protect the base of the inner tube from injury by the inside of the rim.

Development of the Pneumatic Tyre

It must be apparent that if the pneumatic tyre was to come into general use it was important to develop a simple means of mounting and demounting the tyres on the vehicle. A variety of rims was produced from about 1890 onwards. The most successful of these was the 'clincher' rim, used in conjunction with a beaded edge tyre, the projections on which fitted under the rim flanges and were held in place by the internal air pressure. The clincher tyre was gradually superseded by the 'straight-sided' type with the modern wire bead, and rims settled down to the present day well base type for car tyres and the flat base type for giant tyres.

The replacement of square woven fabric by cord fabric started about 1916 and the immediate improvement in casing life soon led to its general adoption. It is very difficult to force rubber into the intersections of warp and weft on a woven fabric, and flexing leads to a sawing action which results in very early failure. Fabric with a warp of cord construction and little or no weft thread may be completely insulated with rubber and the sawing action is non-existent. Rayon has replaced cotton as the casing material to a considerable extent and the new man-made fibres, nylon, Terylene, etc., are now becoming of interest to the tyre designer. In some types of tyres high tensile steel wire is used for the casing structure.

Before 1895, pneumatic tyres were used solely on bicycles and horse-drawn carriages. Their use on a motor vehicle is first recorded in accounts of the Paris-Bordeaux race in June 1895. In Chapter II we have noted the developments in compounding which improved tyre life, and gradually, with due regard for safety, the pneumatic principle was applied to vehicles of increasing size and weight. Demands for increased passenger comfort have resulted in a progressive change from tyres of small section operated at high air pressure to those of increased sectional size and much lower air pressures. A typical car tyre in the 1900's had a rim diameter of 28 in., a section of $2\frac{1}{2}$ in. and an inflation pressure of 50 p.s.i. When we compare these figures with the 13 in. rim diameter, 6 in. section width and 18 to 24 p.s.i. inflation pressure of a popular modern car tyre, the increase in comfort may be readily appreciated.

Manufacture of the Pneumatic Tyre

Premastication of the rubber and the mixing of the various stocks follow conventional practice, internal mixers being used for both operations, although special plasticating machinery is sometimes used. To improve the adhesion of the rubber to the casing, the cord fabric is first treated with a special solution and the rubber coating then applied by calendering. This process is also employed in frictioning and coating bead and chafer fabrics, and for producing the thin

K

sheetings used as insulation between plies. The tread portion of the tyre is extruded through a die to give the required uncured shape and an extruder with a cross or T-head coats the bead wires. Casing plies are cut from calendered cord at the specified bias angle and assembled, in a variety of ways depending on the size and type of tyre, ready for the 'building' process. The plies, beads, insulations, breaker strips, chafers, tread, etc., are now built on to a drum in accordance with the design specification. Great care is exercised in the exact positioning of the components and the thorough consolidation of the complete assembly. The cover is removed from the building drum somewhat in the shape of an open-ended barrel. It is then brought nearer to the shape of the cured tyre by a machine which at the same time fits the curing bag, a heavy type of inner tube which is necessary for applying internal pressure to the hollow casing during moulding. Vulcanisation is done in vertical autoclaves, individual or twin curing units. In autoclave curing the moulds containing the tyres are stacked one on top of the other on the ram. The lid is fitted to the autoclave and hydraulic pressure applied to the ram, thus forcing the column of moulds against the lid and keeping the mould halves tightly closed. Steam circulating in the autoclave supplies the heat for curing, while compressed air or high pressure steam is supplied to the curing bags, thus consolidating the whole assembly as the vulcanisation reaction proceeds. The mould is engraved with the desired tread pattern and the combined heat and pressure forces the rubber to take up the characteristic design. On completion of the curing cycle the autoclave is unloaded and the curing bag is removed from the tyre.

In the press curing method, the mould halves are fixed to the platens. The shaped cover, fitted with its curing bag, is placed in the bottom half of the mould. A steam connection is made to the bag valve and the press is closed by push button. At the end of the specified time, the mould opens automatically and permits removal of the cured tyre. In the latest type of curing unit, a rubber bladder takes the place of the conventional curing bag. The tyre does not require a separate shaping operation and is placed in the unit in the barrel shape in which it leaves the building drum. Closing the mould shapes the cover, while the bladder inflates and serves as a curing bag. When the cure is complete the bladder deflates, the mould opens and the tyre is removed. Trimming precedes a stringent inspection, then follow the final operations of painting, wrapping and dispatch.

It must not be thought that the pneumatic tyre has completely ousted its 'solid' forerunner, which is still used on factory trucks, armoured fighting vehicles ('tanks'), some overhead cranes and as supporting rollers in certain processing plants.

RUBBER FOOTWEAR

Very early in rubber's history its waterproof qualities were made use of in the manufacture of crude shoes; in 1615 it is known that Mexican Indians were employing it in a variety of water-tight articles, including footwear. Complete protection from the rigours of our climate demands both a macintosh and some form of rubber overshoe or galosh, but it is interesting to note that in the early days of rubber manufacture Britain concentrated more on waterproof clothing, while the U.S.A. gave more attention to footwear. The reason for this is no doubt the more severe winters experienced in some parts of the U.S.A. compared to our fairly constant rainfall. The importance of this early development is shown by the fact that the name of our raw material in the plural — 'rubbers' — was, and still is applied in America to what we term galoshes.

The first rubber shoes were crude native products from Brazil made on clay formers. They were eagerly bought when first marketed in 1825. Further supplies were improved in shape by stretching on lasts and, as the demand grew, the lasts were sent out to Brazil where the natives thus produced a much better article than was possible with their own clay formers. These shoes, were, of course, of un-vulcanised rubber with the disadvantages we have already noted. Attempts to improve their serviceability contributed to the discovery of vulcanisation in 1839. Development was thereafter quite rapid and by 1847 there was a considerable export trade from America to the U.K. of rubber overshoes made under Charles Goodyear's patent. Manufacture in the U.K. was therefore contemplated and Scotland was chosen, to prevent infringing Hancock's patent (up to 1852 it was necessary to apply for patents separately in England, Scotland and Ireland). The range of rubber footwear has grown enormously from the early unglamorous overshoe and now comprises galoshes, over-boots, wellingtons and coloured bootlets for women and children. The industrial range includes heavy wellingtons and overboots for outdoor workers, fishermen, firemen, etc., and a safety type with internal steel toecap is now available. The sand shoe, (gym shoe or 'Plimsoll') is still a very popular general purpose sports shoe, although specialised types of shoe are made for most sports.

The components consist of cloth parts, rubber uppers and outsoles, bindings, fabric-backed sponge, moulded rubber heels, and accessories such as rubber adhesives, buckles, slide fasteners, eyelets, etc. The rubber mixes are prepared on conventional mixing machines. The rubber sheets for the outsoles are made on small but sturdily-built four or six bowl calenders, the final bowl being a replaceable engraved roll which produces any desired pattern on the outsole. Other rubber parts are made on ordinary calenders. Stretchy fabrics such as light cotton nets, nylon, etc., are rubbered by the spreading process but heavier fabrics are frictioned or coated by calendering.

Outsoles may be prepared by a power-driven clicking press or cut on a machine in which a sharp knife is guided round a pattern of the desired size and shape. Depending on the volume of production, other parts are cut by machine or hand. As much pre-assembly of these parts as possible is done prior to final assembly on a metal last. Either belt type or endless chain type conveyors are employed in assembly, the former permitting the operator to remove the last from the belt, and replace it when the component has been added, while on the latter the operator works on the shoe as it passes him at reduced speed. The high polish on many types of rubber footwear is given by a special lacquer which is now applied to the uncured shoe. Vulcanisat tion is generally carried out by the 'hot air' method, but a 'direc-moulding' process has been introduced in recent years. In the direct moulding process rubber soles and heels are bonded to leather or canvas uppers in one mechanical operation. The completed upper and insole are removed from the last on which they have been assembled and transferred to another last which forms part of the moulding press. The correct amount of unvulcanised sole and heel compound is placed on the insole and the mould closes over the shoe. The heat and pressure thus moulds, vulcanises and bonds the rubber to the shoe.

CABLES AND ELECTRICAL INSULATION

A cable for carrying electricity consists of a conductor (generally several wires stranded together for compactness and flexibility) insulated with rubber and suitably protected by a cotton braid, a tough rubber sheath or metal armouring, depending on the conditions of service.

All rubbers used for the purpose of electrical insulation must be free from any conductive material or from any substance which might

Fig. 37.   Direct moulding of footwear.

be dissolved out by water. Natural rubber is still popular but where exceptionally good resistance to oil, weather or flame is desired one or other of the synthetic elastomers may be chosen. The rubber is applied to the conductor by extrusion or spiral wrapping, and followed by layers of braid and rubber sheathing as required. Curing is usually done in autoclaves by the 'open steam' method, but for long runs of small cables extrusion may be followed directly by vulcanisation, which is carried out in a long tube containing steam at a pressure of about 200 p.s.i.

BELTING

Belting has two main functions, the carrying of materials (conveyor belting) and the transfer of power (transmission belting).

Conveyor belts consist of a carcass and a cover stock. The carcass carries the load while the rubber cover protects it from abrasive wear, the weather, solvents, acid fumes, etc., to which the belting may be subjected in service. The carcass material is traditionally cotton duck, but rayon, nylon, Terylene, glass fibre and steel cable have all been used. For the cover stock the most suitable rubber is chosen to suit the service conditions, a mix akin to a tyre tread stock finding general application. In manufacture, the frictioned cotton plies are assembled on long tables and passed through consolidating rollers. Belt building machines are available for close control of tension thus ensuring that all plies take their fair share of the load. The calendered cover stock may be applied by hand, or the assembled belt may be passed through the calender and the cover applied directly. Vulcanisation is carried out in large hydraulic presses fitted with devices for tensioning the belt, which is cured in sections equal in length to the press platens. A cooler area is usually arranged at each end of the steam-heated platens to minimise overcure at the overlapping areas. A method of curing, which avoids this overlapping and has many other advantages, is the continuous vulcanisation process in which the belt travels slowly round a number of steam-heated rolls, pressure being obtained by a tensioned steel belt.

Conveyor belting may be made with a flanged edge which prevents materials falling off, or with a corrugated surface which will carry packages up and down inclines without slipping. Passenger conveyor belts are now in operation in several places in the U.S.A., where they are used for transporting large numbers of people at busy railway stations.

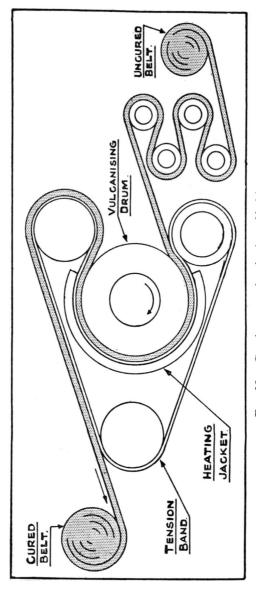

FIG. 38. Continuous vulcanisation of belting.

A considerable mileage of conveyor belting is employed underground in coal mines. A definite fire hazard exists when rubber is used, as it may ignite when a driving drum continues to rotate against a stalled belt. After the Creswell Colliery disaster in 1950, belting manufacturers were asked to develop a non-inflammable belt, and natural rubber has now been largely replaced by PVC and neoprene in this application.

Belting for the transmission of power must be much more flexible than conveyor belting, so that it may adhere to the pulleys and exert its maximum effect. There are three main types — folded edge, where one or more of the fabric plies are brought over the belt edge; raw edge, where the plies stop abruptly at the edge, the belt having been cut to width after cure; cord type, where the reinforcement is in the form of cords, usually cotton, but sometimes rayon, nylon or Terylene.

The V-belt is a transmission belt which operates, usually in multiple, between V-shaped sheaves. The V-type is chosen in preference to a flat transmission belt where space is limited since V-belts can operate efficiently between shorter centres.

Hose and Tubing

This covers a wide variety of sizes and types, ranging from $\frac{1}{8}$ in. bore tubing to 28 in. diameter dredging hose. The type of construction varies, depending on the pressure that the hose has to withstand, from the plain rubber of the garden hose to heavily-reinforced oil-drilling hose which may suffer shock pressures of 5,000 p.s.i. Hose is distinguished from tubing by the presence of a layer of reinforcing material, the purpose of which is to prevent change of shape or size under stresses which would damage a tube.

Tubing and hose consisting of rubber only are extruded by the methods already described and cured by the 'open steam' process. Reinforced hose consists essentially of an inside tube, surrounded by a textile casing and protected by a cover stock.

Wrapped hose is made by building the inner tube from calendered sheet or blowing an extruded tube on to a mandrel. Frictioned woven cotton duck is then applied at an angle of 45° — to give flexibility to the hose — and the cover stock fitted. The assembly is fitted with wrapping cloths and cured in open steam on the mandrel. The laborious operations of applying fabric, cover stock, wrapping and unwrapping may now be done by machine, the mandrel being rotated as the components are fitted.

Woven hose consists of an inner tube (extruded or built from calendered sheet) fitted inside a fabric jacket woven on a circular loom. The tube is given a semi-cure to make it strong enough to withstand pulling inside the textile jacket. The assembly is cured by supplying steam under pressure to the inside of the tube. Fire hose is a typical example of a woven hose.

Braided hose has the textile reinforcement applied by either horizontal or vertical braiding, thin rubber sheet being applied between each layer of braid. The cover stock is fitted either by wrapping or by extrusion through a T-head. The hose is next sheathed in lead by a process of extrusion, except that the lead press uses a piston instead of a screw to force the molten lead around the hose. In its flexible mould the hose is coiled on drums and cured in an autoclave, water pressure being maintained in the hose during cure to consolidate the component parts. After vulcanisation the lead is stripped off and re-used.

All-purpose hose for air, water, oil, petrol and hydraulic lines is now available, the reinforcement being a combination of rayon and wire braid. A self-coiling petrol hose is now being manufactured, this special feature is obtained by fitting to the hose an extra strip of rubber in which is embedded a leaf spring.

CELLULAR RUBBER

This classification comprises two main groups — 'Sponge Rubber', in which the cells communicate with each other, and 'Expanded Rubber' in which the cells are non-intercommunicating, self-contained units. Sponge made from 'dry' rubber has been almost, but not completely, superseded by latex foam rubber made directly from latex. In its turn, latex foam is being seriously challenged by foams made of the polyurethane type of 'plastics'.

The manufacture of conventional sponge rubber is akin to the making of a sponge cake. The porous texture is obtained by mixing into the rubber a substance which gives off a gas during vulcanisation. Baking soda has actually been used for the purpose, but better control of the pore size is given by certain nitrogen-producing substances and these are now in general use. This sponge is made by the ordinary rubber processing methods — the raw rubber is masticated, compounding ingredients are added and vulcanisation carried out in a press or open steam. Latex foam sponge, on the other hand, is made directly from liquid latex thus eliminating the masticating process. Rubber technologists have always considered it illogical to coagulate liquid latex into solid rubber, when the first and very costly processing operation is to soften it again so that the compounding ingredients may be added. The manufacture of foam rubber directly from latex represents the first important break with conventional methods. It has necessitated the provision of facilities for the bulk handling of latex at ports in both producing and consuming countries. The rapid public acceptance of latex foam is due to its supreme comfort-giving properties, as exemplified in such products as bed mattresses, pillows and upholstery generally. This comfort results from the structure of the foam, which consists of a system of interconnected cells of which there may be as many as a quarter of a million in one cubic inch of foam. This structure of highly resilient vulcanised rubber gives uniform support to every part of the weight placed upon it, no matter how unevenly the weight may be distributed, as is the case with the human body.

The process of manufacture is simple to describe, but a high degree of technical skill is required to ensure uniformity in the finished product. As obtained from the tree, latex contains approximately 35% of rubber, suspended as tiny globules in a watery liquid, but to reduce shipping costs the latex is concentrated on the plantation until the rubber content is about 60%.

The necessary compounding ingredients, all in the form of fine water dispersions, are added to the concentrated latex and the mix is then converted into a foam by introducing air, and beating to a consistency not unlike that of whipped cream. The original laboratory batches were made in a small cake-mixing machine, but batch production has given way to continuous foaming carried out in an apparatus based, strangely enough, on a machine for making marshmallows. A quantity of a gelling agent, a material capable of setting the foam after a short controlled interval of time, is now added, and the foam is poured into moulds and the surface levelled off. Vulcanising is carried out at about 212° F, in live steam at atmospheric pressure, after which the article is removed from the mould, washed in water and dried in hot air.

The individual cells of sponge rubber are interconnecting, to a lesser extent in conventional sponge and to a greater extent in latex foam sponge. Expanded rubber, first developed as a puncture-proof filling for tyres, also has a cellular structure but each cell is quite separate from its neighbours. It is made by subjecting the rubber to nitrogen gas under very high pressure. When the pressure is released the rubber expands and produces the cellular structure. Its principal modern use is in the refrigeration industry as a heat-insulating material.

TEXTILE-RUBBER COMPOSITES

Although tyres, belting and hose are composite structures of textile and rubber, the term textile-rubber composite is applied to such products as waterproofs (the rubber 'mac', not the plastic variety) tarpaulins, self-inflating life rafts, survival suits, collapsible flexible containers for the transport of liquids by road or rail, or even by sea. In the last instance the container may be towed behind the ship.

The proofed fabrics used in textile-rubber composites are usually coated by the spreading method, since this is more satisfactory for the fine fabrics which might be damaged by calendering. Proofings may be single texture — a single layer of cloth coated on one side with rubber, or double texture as in the original macintosh, in which there are two layers of fabric with rubber between.

Due to the diversity of size and shape of the products, and the accuracy with which some, say anti-G suits for airmen, must be constructed, assembly by hand rather than by machine is still necessary.

Ordinary proofings are still vulcanised by the 'cold cure' process. This, as we know, means that sulphur is not mixed with the rubber in the usual way. The vulcanising agent, which is applied to the surface of the rubbered cloth, is the liquid sulphur monochloride diluted with naphtha. When a normal sulphur mix has been used, curing is carried out by the 'hot air' method. Very fast accelerators are now available which make a separate vulcanisation process unnecessary. Curing takes place in the rubbered fabric in a few days, when it is left at normal temperatures.

EBONITE

Ebonite (vulcanite or hard rubber) is the hard product obtained by vulcanising a rubber compound which contains a much higher proportion of sulphur than in ordinary rubber mixes. Although the ebonite manufacturing section of the rubber industry has suffered somewhat from the competition of plastics, ebonite is still considered by many chemical engineers to be the most suitable material for pumps, pipe fittings, tank linings, and other products which require good resistance to attack by chemicals. Outside this field, it is much used in combs, pen and pencil parts, pipe stems and knife handles.

Ebonite may be used to make a mould for simple types of rubber mats. A cured mat is pressed into a slab of uncured ebonite, it is then given sufficient cure to enable the mat to be stripped off, and the ebonite is then cured to the hard stage. A similar technique is used in the repairing of tyres. A 'matrix' of a portion of the tread is made and this is used as a mould to reproduce the pattern at the area which is being repaired.

FLOORING, TILING AND ROADS

Rubber has been in use as a flooring material for about sixty years. It is resilient, quiet, hygienic and extremely durable, but care is required in the preparation of the surface on which it is to be laid. Its initial cost is somewhat higher than that of other forms of floor covering, but this is offset by its long life — the black and white tiles which form the flooring of the Mitchell Library in Glasgow were laid about fifty years ago and their condition is still excellent, except that the white rubber has worn rather more quickly than the black.

The term flooring generally refers to continuous lengths of calendered sheet, up to six feet wide, laid in large sections in the same way as for linoleum. Tiling describes separate squares, diamonds and various other shapes, which are assembled in the desired pattern on the actual site. Both types can be obtained with a layer of sponge rubber backing, which further increases their cushioning effect.

Manufacture follows conventional methods, but the machines used must be large enough to enable economic widths and lengths to be handled. The mixes used do not generally contain more than about 25% of rubber, heavy loading with the filler type of compounding ingredients being necessary to limit the liveliness of the rubber and prevent creep. The calendering is fairly simple, provided the mechanical condition of the machine is such as to ensure uniform thickness across the whole width of the sheet. In preparing the attractive marbled and mottled effects, care is necessary in placing the 'runners' of differently coloured rubbers, so that the design may be fairly uniform throughout its entire length. Flooring is vulcanised in large presses as used for belting, but the continuous vulcanising method (by 'Rotocure' machine) can also be employed.

Tiles are made in the same way as flooring. They may be either cut out from vulcanised sheet or cured separately in moulds.

Rubber latex may be combined with Portland cement and an aggregate such as cork, sand or sawdust in making an abrasion resistant flooring, which has excellent adhesion to any type of surface. The floor need not necessarily have an even surface, since the mix is trowelled on and thus takes up all irregularities.

The original method of employing rubber in roads was to lay it in the form of moulded blocks. This method has now given way to the use of the rubber in powder form, which is mixed with the tar or bitumen before application to the road surface. The rubber may be natural or synthetic, and vulcanised tyre tread crumb has also been used. In addition to the use of rubberised bitumen, rubber chips may also be rolled in, giving a durable and yet safe surface for such uses as children's playgrounds.

MECHANICALS

Mechanical rubber goods are those used in engineering and the machinery employed in industry. Belting and hose which, of course, fit this description are not usually included in this group, which comprises gaskets and oil seals of various types, rubber rollers and roll coverings, anti-vibration units, air suspension units for trucks and the amazing variety of automobile rubber parts. On a modern car these rubber parts may number 500 and weigh as much as 100 lb., excluding the weight of tyres and tubes. For many mechanicals it is necessary to bond the rubber to metal. The techniques of transfer and injection moulding (discussed in Chapter VIII) may be employed in addition to conventional compression moulding.

LATEX

We have already noted that it is illogical to take fluid latex and convert it to solid rubber, when for many manufacturing purposes it must again be brought to a softer or even liquid form. It is only within the last twenty-five years or so, however, that processes have been developed to make the best use of latex, since the techniques employed demand a higher degree of process control than do those for dry rubber manufacture. The direct uses of latex are in latex foam, dipped goods (formerly made exclusively from rubber solution), as the binder for rubberised hair and non-woven fabrics, and as a component of the latex-resorcinol-formaldehyde (LRF) solution used in the treatment of rayon tyre cords. It should be remembered that most synthetic rubbers are available in the form of latices.

Natural rubber latex putrifies very quickly after leaving the tree and must be preserved by the addition of ammonia. Furthermore, as

FIG. 39. Latex foam manufacture.

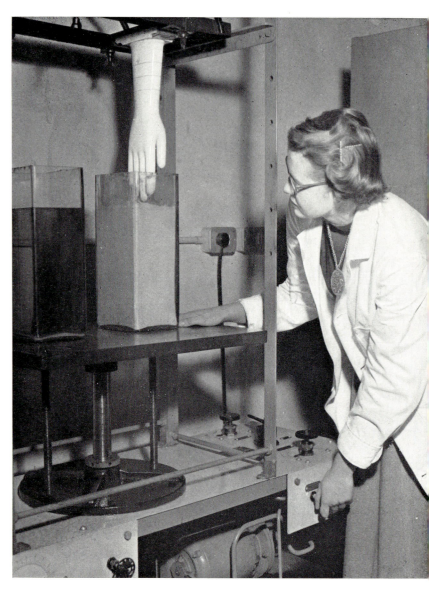

Fig. 40.   Experimental latex dipping.

the latex contains only about 40% of rubber, some degree of concentration is required. It is quite uneconomic to transport the 60% of water from the country of origin to the country of manufacture. Concentration is carried out by four methods:

(a) Creaming, in which the preserved latex is allowed to stand until the lighter rubber particles rise to the surface. Natural creaming is slow and the process is usually speeded up by the addition of certain substances which exist in a very fine state of division ('colloidal' substances), e.g. sodium alginate, tapioca flour.

(b) Centrifuging employs a machine similar to a milk separator. The latex is whirled round very rapidly, the heavier water is thrown to the outer diameter of the centrifuge and the lighter rubber particles collect in the centre.

(c) In electro-decantation the latex is subjected to the passage of an electric current. The tiny rubber particles, which carry a negative charge of electricity, move toward the positively-charged electrode, the 'anode'.

(d) In the evaporation process, some of the water is driven off by very careful heating, after stabilising agents have been added to the latex.

Strange as it may seem, latex can be vulcanised without any change in outward appearance. It remains fluid and may be processed normally, yet drying of the film at quite low temperatures gives a fully vulcanised product.

The compounding of latex follows the principles of dry rubber compounding, with rubber curatives, softeners, and a filler (if needed), but there are two important differences in preparing the mixture, (i) latex consists of particles suspended in a watery fluid, and (ii) latex is a colloidal dispersion with electrically-charged particles. It follows that, with a few exceptions, all compounding ingredients to be added to latex must be in a fine state of division and prepared in the form of a liquid dispersion. If solid ingredients are added directly, a proper mixture is not obtained and coagulation will probably result. The addition of ammonia on the plantation gives sufficient stability to the latex to keep it in good condition during transit and storage, but it is almost always necessary to add further stabilisers before manufacturing commences.

In bringing about the necessary fine state of division of compounding ingredients and their dispersion in water, use is made of cone mills, colloid mills or other proprietary mills which repeatedly pass the powder and water at high speed through fine orifices and thus mix them intimately. The ball mill, often used in this work, consists of a cylindrical vessel containing a number of porcelain balls, which bring about the grinding action by rolling over each other as the cylinder is rotated.

MISCELLANEOUS

We have by no means exhausted the variety of rubber products — printers' rollers and blankets, chemical plant lining, cut thread and tape, sports accessories, adhesives and adhesive tape, hot water bottles — but the student should remember that his practical instruction includes the moulding of simple products, plying up belts and fitting with covers, building on mandrels, manufacture of bladders and hollow rubber balls, dipping, latex compounding and latex foam manufacture. This instruction, combined with the descriptions of manufacturing methods given here and in the references at the end of the chapter, should enable the student to understand without difficulty the methods of manufacture of other products which we have not specifically mentioned.

Solvents

This short note on solvents is included since they are extensively used in the assembly of uncured rubber components. A solvent is a substance, usually liquid, within which another substance is dissolved. They are employed in 'washing' uncured rubber surfaces. This restores tack and ensures that the junction with another component will be sound and will not separate, either during vulcanisation or during the service life of the product. When washing with solvent does not give sufficient adhesion, the surface may be painted with a rubber 'solution' (sometimes termed rubber 'cement'), which is a dispersion of uncured rubber, either natural or synthetic, in a suitable solvent. Other uses of rubber solutions are in floor laying, sticking on shoe soles, and as temporary adhesives in assembly operations in many industries. In the proofing of fabrics by the spreading process, the 'dough' used is a 25% to 30% dispersion of rubber in solvent.

Nomenclature of solvents is somewhat confused, since chemical names, commercial names, trade names and popular abbreviations are all used, e.g. the commercial variety of the pure chemical substance benzene is termed 'benzol', carbon tetrachloride is usually abbreviated to 'carbon tet', methyl ethyl ketone is popularly MEK. The name 'benzine' refers to a spirit prepared from petroleum and must not be confused with the coal tar derivative, benzene. Another abbreviation met with is SBP followed by the numbers 1 to 6. This refers to petroleum distillates with special boiling points, a property which is related to the speed of evaporation of a solvent and therefore its rate of drying. The higher the B.P. the slower the evaporation of a solvent.

The ideal solvent for rubber should have the following properties: (i) it must show chemical stability to rubber (ii) it should have a restricted distillation range (neither too volatile nor too resistant to evaporation), (iii) its odour should not be too unpleasant and (iv) it should have no poisonous (toxic) effects on human beings.

Coal tar solvents are obtained from the tarry substance produced by the distillation of coal. They consist of the substances benzene, toluene and xylene, the commercial varieties of which are known respectively as benzol, toluol and xylol.

Natural petroleum is a valuable source of rubber solvents of all degrees of volatility. Distillation produces a number of fractions, each of which is treated to remove those materials which would decrease its efficiency in a particular application. The increased demand for motor spirit has led to the commercial development of 'cracking', whereby, under the influence of high temperatures and pressures, large molecules of higher boiling point fractions are broken down into smaller molecules whose boiling points lie within the motor spirit range. Petroleum solvents are not quite as effective solvents for rubber as are coal tar solvents, but they are less toxic; it is for this reason that petroleum rubber solvent (PRS) has largely replaced coal tar naphtha.

The chlorinated solvents, carbon tetrachloride and trichloro-ethylene are noted for their non-flammability — they actually extinguish flame, but the vapours are toxic and precautions against inhaling them must be taken.

Carbon disulphide, the traditional solvent for sulphur mono-chloride in the cold cure process of vulcanising, will not be discussed since its use for this purpose is now illegal, due to its extremely toxic nature.

Toxicity simply means 'poisonous effect' and very stringent regulations as to the use of solvents in industry are laid down and enforced by law. A distinction is sometimes made between those solvents which can produce definite and irreparable harm to the human body and those which have only a temporary effect. It must be emphasised, however, that care is necessary in handling all solvents and the statutory regulations must be complied with.

The flammability of most solvents again requires the utmost care in handling. The 'flash point' is an index of the flammability of a liquid. It is determined by heating a measured volume of the solvent at a standard rate and applying a test flame at intervals until the vapour ignites. Liquids with flash points below 73° F are classed as 'highly inflammable' and there are special laws regarding handling and storage; even small quantities of these requiring appropriate labelling. There is less difficulty with liquids having a flash point above 73° F but care is still needed. All coal tar and petroleum solvents will burn if deliberately set alight.

Rubber Solutions

The preparation of rubber solutions requires efficient premastication of the rubber, whereby the structure is broken down to a considerable degree. When unmilled, crude rubber behaves in solvents somewhat like vulcanised rubber, but when well masticated it swells to an unlimited extent, gradually diffusing throughout the whole liquid and forming a comparatively viscous solution. For a given concentration of rubber in solvent, increase in mastication time results in reduced viscosity, i.e. it gives a 'thinner' solution.

Solvent Recovery

The importance of solvent recovery is obvious. If the solvents are permitted to escape into the atmosphere, it is not only very wasteful, but may cause fire and explosion as well as injury to the health of the operatives. The solvents used in rubber spreading and dipping are invariably recovered for re-use.

The process comprises two operations — the adsorption of the solvent vapour by a special form of carbon ('activated carbon'), and the recovery of the solvent from the carbon. The vapour containing the solvent is collected from hoods over the spreading machine and dipping tanks, and passed into a container filled with active carbon. When this has been charged to its maximum, the solvent laden atmosphere is diverted to a second container, while the solvent is being recovered from the first. This is done by blowing steam through the carbon and passing the steam and solvent to a condenser. Here the steam and solvent condense and the solvent is separated from the water by suitable means. Hot air is passed through the carbon to dry it, after which the process may be repeated.

Active carbon may be made from almost any vegetable matter, coconut shells, wood, peat or coal. These materials are carbonised at a high temperature, in the absence of oxygen, and are then activated by zinc chloride or phosphoric acid. Active carbon contains countless numbers of very fine capillaries, which have an immense area in proportion to the weight of material (1 cc. may contain pores having a total wall area of about 600 sq. m.). Solvent recovery by active carbon is an adsorption process. Absorption of, say, water by a sponge takes place throughout the whole volume of the sponge. Adsorption is a surface effect, and obviously an increase in surface area for a given weight of substance will magnify the effect enormously.

REFERENCES

GENERAL

The Story of Rubber. Educational Productions Ltd., London
The Fundamentals of Rubber Technology. Imperial Chemical Industries Ltd., Dyestuffs Division, Manchester
SEAMAN, R. G. and MERRILL, A. M., Machinery and Equipment for Rubber and Plastics. *Rubber World*. Vol. I.
Vanderbilt Rubber Handbook. 1958, New York, U.S.A.

TYRES

Making a Car Tyre. Dunlop Rubber Co. Ltd., London
LAMBOURN, L. J., The Indispensable Pneumatic Tyre. *Trans. Inst. Rubber Ind.* 1958, Vol. 34, 118
WOODS, E. C., *Pneumatic Tyre Design*. Institution of the Rubber Industry

FOOTWEAR

Making Footwear with Rubber. Dunlop Rubber Co. Ltd., London

CABLES

EVANS, B. B., Processes and Materials for Rubber Cables. *Trans. Inst. Rubber Ind.* 1953, Vol. 29, 42

BELTING

Conveyor Belting. Dunlop Rubber Co. Ltd., Liverpool

HOSE

Industrial Hose. Goodyear Tyre & Rubber Co. Ltd., Wolverhampton

ROADS

Rubber in Roads. Natural Rubber Bureau, London

MECHANICALS

BUCHAN, S., New Methods of Moulding. *Trans. Inst. Rubber Ind.* 1946, Vol. 22, 41

Buchan, S., *Rubber to Metal Bonding*. 2nd ed. 1959, London
Westhead, J., Chemical Plant Lining. *Proc. Inst. Rubber Ind.* 1961, Vol. 8, 121

LATEX

Stern, H. J., *Practical Latex Work*. Leicester
Natural Rubber Latex and its Applications. Nos. 1, 2, 3, 4 and 5, Natural Rubber Bureau, London

CHAPTER XIII

THE TESTING OF RUBBER AND RUBBER PRODUCTS

The importance of rubber testing to industry in general is such that many test methods are issued as specifications by the British Standards Institution, the American Society for Testing and Materials and the corresponding bodies in other countries. Also the development of new tests and the improvement of existing ones are constantly under consideration by the Rubber Committee of the International Organisation for Standardisation.

Rubber is a fickle substance. The raw material varies and processing may introduce further variation, which, fortunately, can be smoothed out in the cured product. Tests have been devised to measure all such variation and deterioration, thus enabling suitable corrective action to be taken in the factory to improve the uniformity and serviceability of the finished article.

The testing carried out in any rubber factory may be considered under three heads,

(a) testing of raw materials,
(b) testing of materials in process of manufacture
(c) testing of the finished product.

All raw rubbers, the wide variety of compounding ingredients, the solvents, textile materials, etc., are tested to ensure that they conform to the purchase specification. In general, the standard methods of chemical analysis, which determine the kinds and amounts of different substances present, are used, with certain additional tests necessitated by the use of the material in rubber, e.g. constancy of colour, fastness to light and to vulcanising conditions for colouring materials. The development of equipment for the very accurate measurement of minute quantities of chemical substances has recently speeded up the tedious operations of analysis. This technique of 'micro-analysis' is being used increasingly. In the evaluation of raw rubber chemical testing alone is not sufficient. It is also necessary to mix samples with the correct amounts of curing ingredients on a laboratory-size mill, vulcanise test slabs and carry out tensile strength tests on accurately dimensioned rings or strips cut from the slabs. By stretching the test piece on a machine and making certain measurements, the technologist obtains a curve showing the relationship between the load applied to the test-piece and the corresponding stretch. The shape of this stress/strain curve is then compared with that of a curve from a standard sample of rubber.

In common with industry in general, the rubber factory depends for its efficient functioning on each department supplying processed material of uniform quality, ready for the next step in the manufacturing process. Except in those branches of our industry which use rubber in the form of latex, the raw material must be softened before it is possible to incorporate the compounding ingredients. The degree of softness or 'plasticity' of both the raw rubber and of the finished mix is vital to the success of all the succeeding factory operations, and therefore close control is essential. Finished stock must also be uniformly mixed and have the correct rate of vulcanisation. The testing necessary to ensure that these conditions are satisfied involves plasticity measurements on samples of raw rubber and unvulcanised mixed stock. It is also necessary to determine the specific gravity of vulcanised mixed stock and to carry out a tensile strength test, which in this case is modified for speedy operation. Where very fast curing mixes are employed processing difficulty may be experienced due to premature vulcanisation or 'scorching', and routine checking is necessary. Small samples of the mix are heated for increasing periods of time, until the original plasticity is gradually replaced by the elasticity which develops as the vulcanisation reaction proceeds. Further testing of material during the manufacturing process will depend on the product. For instance it is necessary to test viscosity of rubber solutions and latex in the manufacture of dipped goods, and the elongation of rubber coated fabric in tyre and belting manufacture, etc.

Finished product testing should begin with a check on the dimensions and positioning of the components of the article in order to ensure that it meets the design requirements, and that its state of cure is satisfactory. The product or suitably shaped sections of it, depending on whether it is composed entirely of rubber or contains a textile material, may be subjected to an astonishing variety of tests. It may be stretched, compressed, sheared and torn apart from its fabric or metal components; it may be flexed rapidly to induce cracking, oscillated under load to determine how fast it builds up heat, 'weathered' either outdoors, or indoors in cabinets with controlled weather conditions. It may be subjected to any one of the separate factors responsible for the deterioration of rubber — heat, light, oxygen, ozone, oils — or may be given a general 'accelerated ageing' test which speeds up natural perishing. This test, in the case of particular products, and after years of experience, can be used to predict service life. Considerable ingenuity has been shown in devising machines which will test the product under conditions as near as possible to those found in actual service, e.g. a 'walking' machine has been used for evaluating the wear of rubber footwear, flexing machines for wear and ply separation of rubber belts and hoses, wheels for destructive tests on tyres, etc. When such tests are not considered sufficiently informative, manufacturers do not hesitate to test their products under actual service conditions and, to this end, tyre manufacturers run fleets of test cars, footwear manufacturers employ operatives to walk certain routes daily, and makers of clothes wringers themselves operate small laundries.

Following this resumé of testing in general, we must enumerate all the common tests applied to rubber and select for detailed description those which are required by the 'City and Guilds' syllabus; the full treatment of rubber testing would occupy many volumes.

A. PROCESSABILITY TESTS

(i) *Plasticity or Viscosity*
(ii) *Scorch characteristics*
(iii) *Rate of Cure*

B. VULCANISATE TESTS

(i) *Tensile stress/strain properties*
(ii) *Hardness*
(iii) *Tear resistance*
(iv) *Abrasion resistance*
(v) *Resistance to flex-cracking and fatigue*
(vi) *Permanent set*
(vii) *Heat build-up and resilience*
(viii) *Resistance to ageing and weathering*
(ix) *Chemical resistance*
(x) *High temperature and low temperature properties*

(xi) *Electrical properties*
(xii) *Determination of specific gravity*

We will consider in some detail all the processability tests and items (i), (ii), (vi), (viii) and (xii) of the tests on vulcanised rubber. Mention of the others will be made and the references at the end of the chapter will assist those who wish greater detail.

The reasons for controlling the factors which affect the 'processability' of a rubber compound have been explained at length in Chapter VII.

(i) *Plasticity Testing*

If space were available it would be interesting to trace the development of instruments for the measurement of plasticity. They range from the original 'Williams', through several modified 'Williams' types, 'Goodrich', modified 'Goodrich' and 'Scott', to the modern 'Wallace Rapid' and 'Mooney Viscometer', the latter now pneumatically operated and fully instrumented.

All plastometers are based on one or other of three principles, namely, compression, rotation or extrusion. These three principles can be considered as corresponding to the operations of moulding, milling and extrusion respectively. No single instrument, however, can measure all the rheological properties which contribute to processability ('rheology' is the study of the flow characteristics of materials).

The determination of plasticity and recovery using a compression type instrument is fully described in BS 1673: Part 3: 1951. The original method of operating the 'Williams' had several disadvantages, amongst these were the length of time taken to prepare the specimen pellets, the necessity for opening the oven door to insert and remove samples, and the difficulty of making an accurate recovery measurement. Most of these problems have been overcome in later models. This instrument measures the 'plasticity number', which is the thickness of the pellet in hundredths of a millimetre after compression for three minutes at a temperature of either 158° F or 212° F (depending on the particular compound), under a load of 5 kg. If a recovery measurement is required, the load is removed from the pellet, which is allowed to cool for one minute and the 'recovered height' determined.

The Mooney instrument is the only rotation type of plastometer in common use. It is often referred to as a 'Viscometer' since its mode of operation is considered by some technologists to measure viscosity rather than plasticity ('viscosity' is that property of a fluid whereby it tends to resist relative motion within itself). A complete description of the instrument and its use is given in BS 1673: Part 3: 1951. Mooney viscosities are given in units, read from a scale which indicates the drag (strictly speaking, the 'torque') applied to a small mushroom-shaped rotor, turning at a speed of 2 r.p.m. within a sample of the

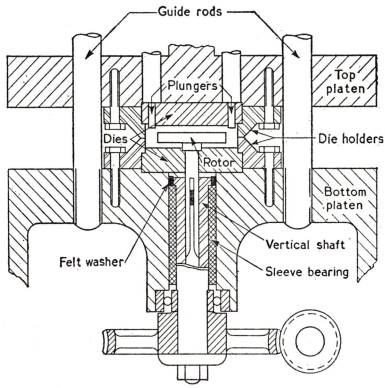

FIG. 41.   Mooney Viscometer.

rubber under test. The chamber in which the rubber is contained is maintained at a specified temperature, usually 212° F. The ordinary Mooney Viscometer is not suited to measure recovery although modified instruments are available which will measure this property. After its selection in World War II as the 'standard' control instrument at all synthetic rubber producing plants, the 'Mooney' became very popular and has now displaced compression plastometers at all factories where large numbers of plasticity measurements must be made.

Although instruments using the extrusion principle are called 'plastometers', they really measure only 'extrudability' and not plasticity. The Firestone plastometer is one instrument specially designed to measure extrudability under widely varying conditions, but a conventional laboratory type extruder may also be used. Results are expressed as the volume extruded in a given time, various corrections being applied for die swell, length shrinkage, etc. A specially-shaped die, a 'Garvey' die, may be used in the extruder head and an index given to the compound after an examination of the extruded section for porosity and for condition of sharp edges, and rounded corners.

(ii) Scorch Characteristics

The object of making a scorch test is to find out just how long a particular compound can be held at a given processing temperature, before the onset of vulcanisation makes further processing difficult or impossible. A once popular method was to cure samples of the compound in the form of tensile test slabs for a range of times at the expected processing temperature, say 220° F. Since warm uncured rubber does not readily part from a mould surface, the scorch index

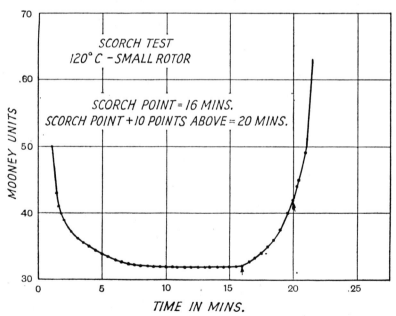

Fig. 42.   Scorch curve.

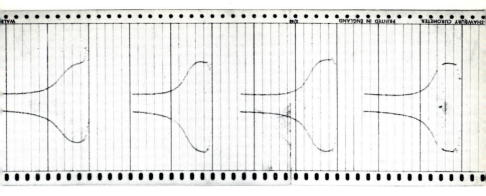

FIG. 43.   Wallace-Shawbury curometer.

FIG. 44.   Typical Curometer traces.

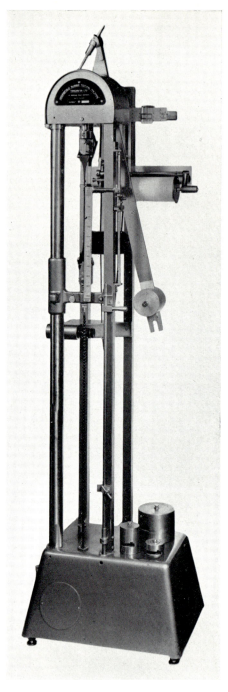

FIG. 45. Hounsfield Tensometer.

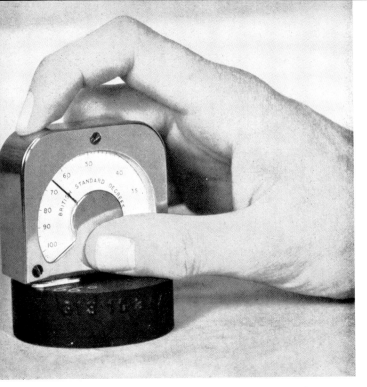

FIG. 46.
Wallace pocket
hardness meter.

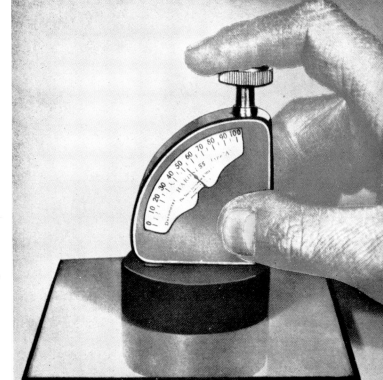

FIG. 47.
Shore durometer.

FIG. 48.—Dupont Crowdon abrasion testing machine.

was taken as the least time of heating which would produce a slab which would leave the mould fairly easily. This method is rather laborious and scorch testing is now done on a plastometer of either the compression or rotation types. The pellets used for the compression test are preheated for a range of times at the desired temperature, and the measurements are made as for a plasticity test. The results are drawn on a graph, if necessary, and clearly show the onset of scorching. It is even simpler on the Mooney Viscometer; the test is run in the usual way but at a higher temperature, say 250° F, and for a longer time, readings of torque being taken at suitable intervals. Again, graphing the results will show at what time the torque has increased quite suddenly as the plasticity is suppressed and elasticity develops.

(iii) *Rate of Cure*

This is defined as the time required to reach a certain state of cure compared to the time required by a standard compound to reach a similar state of cure. While the terms 'undercure', 'overcure', 'correct cure', are easily understood, the meaning of state of cure is more difficult to get over at technician level. It depends on the arbitrary selection of the values obtained by measuring some physical property of a series of samples of a compound, which have been vulcanised for different periods of time, so chosen as to range from undercure to overcure. This will be clearer after we have discussed the stress-strain relationships of vulcanised rubber. There are many other ways, both chemical and physical, of determining state of cure but most are beyond the scope of our syllabus. Since the speed with which a compound reaches a given state of cure is closely bound up with scorch, processability, good mould flow, etc., the cure characteristics may be evaluated on an ordinary Mooney Viscometer. A new instrument, the 'Wallace-Shawbury Curometer' has recently been put on the market. It is claimed that it will give all the information required for the evaluation of rate of cure and state of cure in a much shorter time than on other instruments. It uses less rubber and is much more convenient than those instruments which require the lengthy stress-strain testing of a range of cures.

C. VULCANISATE PROPERTIES

(i) *Tensile stress-strain properties*

Stress is defined as the force inside a body resisting a change of shape; the change of shape is termed 'strain'. Materials may be subjected to a variety of deforming forces, (see Fig. 49), indeed, in engineering applications compression and shear are much more important than extension, although it is the last that concerns us here. The phrase 'tensile stress-strain characteristics of vulcanised rubber' implies stretching a sample of rubber in some apparatus which enables us to record the load we are applying, measuring the strain (elongation) produced by that load and displaying the results in

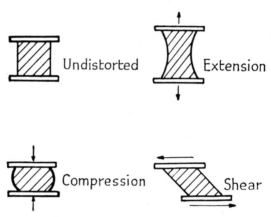

FIG. 49.   Deformation of rubber.

the form of a graph (see Appendix A). The sample of rubber may be stretched to its breaking point or the test may be stopped before this point, depending on the information we are looking for. In drawing such stress-strain curves it is customary to show the stress on the vertical axis and the strain on the horizontal axis. The shape of the curve is characteristic of the kinds and amounts of the compounding ingredients used in the mix, and also of its state of cure. (Fig. 13). The stress is expressed as pounds per square inch (p.s.i.) or as kilograms per square centimetre. It is calculated as the load per unit area of the original (unstretched) sample cross-section, the width and thickness of which must be known. The strain is determined by measuring the distance between two bench marks on the sample and expressing the increase over the original distance as a percentage, thus

$$\text{Elongation} \ (\%) = \frac{\text{Increase in length}}{\text{original length}} \times 100$$

The elongation reached when the sample breaks is referred to as 'elongation at break' or 'ultimate elongation'. It should be noted that when a sample of a metal is subjected to tensile stresses and the corresponding strains measured, the stress-strain 'curve' is (within the limits of elasticity of the metal) a straight line, i.e. the ratio stress/strain is a constant, which is given the name 'modulus of elasticity'. In rubber the ratio of stress to strain is not constant, but varies widely at different parts of the curve. The term 'modulus' in rubber technology is simply the load expressed in pounds per square inch or kilograms per square centimetre required to stretch the rubber to a specified elongation; the elongation must always be stated — otherwise the expression is meaningless. The modulus of a rubber can be regarded as an index of its stiffness or resistance to extension.

Stress-strain curves are obtained by stretching (breaking, or 'pulling') cured specimens on tensile testing machines, of which there are a dozen or so varieties in common use. Samples may be in the form of plain strips, strips with widened ends ('dumb-bell' strips) or rings. Machines vary in the method of reading the elongation of the strip and the applied load. Some types have an autographic fitment which draws the stress-strain curve as the sample is being stretched. Fig. 45 shows one type of tensile tester, the 'Hounsfield Tensometer'. For some purposes it is unnecessary to obtain the full curve, e.g. a popular control for mixed stock is to vulcanise a ring sample for a short time and measure the load required to stretch it to a given elongation, i.e. measure its modulus. The machine stops when the desired elongation is reached, the load reading is shown on a scale. Anyone who has operated a tensile tester using strips, will know how difficult it is to get an exact reading of elongation as the sample is stretching. It is much more accurate to apply a definite stress to the sample and after a specified time measure, on the stationary strip, the elongation produced. There are several types of machines now available which carry out this 'strain' testing.

(ii) *Hardness*

The hardness of vulcanised rubber is defined as the relative resistance to penetration of a blunt point impressed on its surface. Thirty years work, instigated by the RAPRA, and later with the collaboration of all other authorities concerned in rubber testing, has culminated first in the adoption of a standard scale (British Standard Degrees) and finally of International Rubber Hardness Degrees (I.R.H.D.) The test is a simple one to carry out, indeed misleadingly simple, one jabs a needle into a rubber surface and reads a scale. At the moment, however, there are dozens of types of hardness meters in common use and it is most essential that the hardness figure quoted also states the particular instrument used. The most convenient hardness testers are the spring-loaded pocket types, such as the Shore 'Durometer' and the 'Wallace', but for very accurate work and for checking the pocket meters, dead-load bench models are available. It should be noted that the 'Pusey and Jones Plastometer' is really a dead-load hardness tester of the indentation type.

(iii) *Tear Resistance*

High resistance to tearing is obviously desirable in such products as tyre inner tubes and hot water bottles. Also it is thought that tear contributes to the wearing-away of the rubber used in tyre treads and conveyor belt covers. Tear resistance is rather difficult to define precisely but may be described as the resistance to the growth of a cut when tension is applied to the cut. Some tests measure the force required to start a tear, others the force necessary to keep it going once it has started. Older technologists often made estimates of tear resistance by a hand tear test, in which a stretched strip of rubber was nicked with scissors and then watched in order to see the way in which the cut grew. Nowadays tear test pieces, 'crescent', 'angle' or 'tongue-shear', are broken on a tensile tester and the result expressed in pounds required to tear a sample one inch thick.

(iv) *Abrasion Resistance*

Good resistance to abrasion contributes to the long life of tyres, soles and heels, but in these products many other factors such as flexing have to be taken into consideration. Although there are many abrasion testing machines in common use, no manufacturer would dare put a new compound into service on the basis of such laboratory results alone. The Dupont Abrader (also known as the 'Grasselli' or 'Williams') is the machine most likely to be available to the student. Two moulded samples are held against an abrasive wheel and the results are expressed as the volume loss per horsepower-hour of work done on the samples. A new compound is usually rated in relation to a control compound with known abrasion resistance, frequent checking of the control stock being necessary. The 'Lambourn' machine, on which the 'slip' between sample and abrasive wheel can be controlled, is claimed to give good correlation with road testing of tyres.

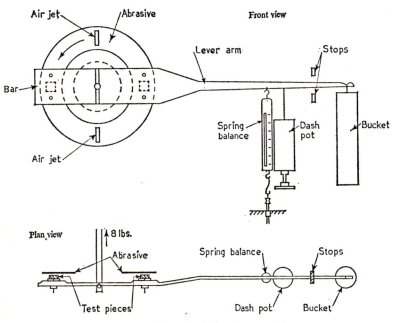

FIG. 50.   Principle of abrasion machine.

(v) *Resistance to Flex-cracking and Fatigue*

The failure of a rubber component may result from the formation and subsequent growth of surface cracks. Again, there are many machines available for measuring this property, the best known being the 'De Mattia' type. The ends of specially-shaped test pieces are fitted between two gripping bars one of which may be oscillated at high speed, usually 300 cycles per minute. While under test, the samples are alternately bent double and pulled almost straight. At regular intervals, depending on the compound, the samples are examined for signs of cracking and are finally given ratings on a scale ranging from 0, which indicates no cracking, to 10, which indicates that the sample has broken as a result of excessive cracking.

(vi) *Permanent Set*

When an elastic material fails to return exactly to its original dimensions after it has been extended, compressed or sheared, we say that it has taken a 'set'. If a strip of vulcanised rubber is stretched and the load later removed, it will return fairly quickly to nearly its original size, but the approach to its final or 'permanent set' will be very much slower. The measurement of permanent set is a good indication (when related to the other tensile properties) of the state of cure of a compound, but what we really measure is the 'sub-permanent set', i.e. the set after a specified time of retraction, since the attainment of the true permanent set is so very slow. Permanent set is described in the same way as elongation, in other words as the increase in length expressed as a percentage of the original length.

The set taken up by a rubber in compression, the 'compression set' may be measured similarly. It is the amount by which a rubber sample fails to return to its original height after being loaded for a specified time. Control of compression set is essential in such products as machine mountings and bearing pads, where excessive settling down might result in serious misalignment of the machinery.

(vii) *Heat Build-up and Resilience*

These are the first dynamic properties of rubber that we have considered. So far we have dealt only with static properties. When we change the shape of a piece of vulcanised rubber, say by repeated flexing or by striking it a blow, heat is generated and there is a consequent rise in temperature of the rubber. The amount of heat generated depends on the compound, its state of cure and just how the rubber is being deformed. Heat build-up is measured on a machine, called a 'flexometer', which applies to the rubber test-piece both a compressive load and a high frequency cyclic compression. The rise in temperature is measured by a thermocouple needle (see Appendix C) inserted in the rubber.

A highly resilient material is one which uses up most of the energy expended in deforming it, in springing back to its former shape. Resilience may therefore be described as the ratio of the energy returned to the energy input, expressed as a percentage. In the case of rubber, some of the energy input is always used up in generating heat. Of course the greater the energy returned, the higher the resilience, and the smaller will be the amount of energy available for heat generation. Therefore the higher the resilience of a compound the cooler it will run. It is obviously desirable that compounds for such uses as tyre treads, transmission belts and roller covering should be designed to have as high resilience as possible, provided other service conditions are met. Resilience is usually measured by the rebound of a pendulum, two well-known machines being the 'Lupke Resiliometer' and the 'Dunlop Tripsometer'.

(viii) *Resistance to ageing and weathering*

We have made frequent mention of the various deteriorating influences which contribute to the ageing and weathering of rubber, a subject ably dealt with in J. M. Buist's Monograph noted in the references. Here we are concerned with the accelerated ageing tests carried out by the manufacturer to give him some idea of the expected service life of his product. All accelerated ageing tests have their limitations and, although some laboratories know by long experience that a certain time of exposure to a particular deteriorating influence will correspond to so many years in service, great care must be taken in applying such formulas generally.

In carrying out an ageing test, suitable samples are exposed to the particular influence or a combination of influences under controlled conditions. Samples are withdrawn at given intervals and their properties compared with those of the unaged specimens. Although it has limitations, it is customary to use the drop in tensile strength as the standard measure of deterioration.

One means of testing is by the 'air oven' method (often called the 'Geer Oven', after its originator, W. C. Geer) in which samples are exposed to air at a temperature of, usually, 158° F. The duration of test may be fourteen days, samples being removed every two days. Higher temperatures may be used but, with some rubbers, results can be misleading.

Since fourteen days is rather a long time to wait for results, a speedier apparatus was devised, the 'Oxygen Bomb'. Here the samples are exposed to oxygen at a pressure of 300 lbs. p.s.i. and 158° F, the time of test being reduced to a few days.

An even more severe test, taking only a few hours, is the air bomb or 'Air Pressure Heat Test'. Air at a pressure of 80 lbs. p.s.i. is used but at a much higher temperature, 260° F, than in either the air oven or oxygen bomb methods.

It is modern practice in these tests to use separate containers for samples when it is known that there is a possibility of contamination. Certain antioxidants, for instance, may be driven off by the heat of the test and pass from one sample to another, thus invalidating the results.

The gas ozone which is present in the atmosphere in varying small concentrations has a very destructive effect on rubber, and test methods are available for the laboratory evaluation of ozone resistance. For general weathering resistance, samples are often exposed on a roof, with or without glass protection. For greater control of weathering, cabinets are available in which special lamps imitate the effect of sunlight, and exposure to 'rain' may also be arranged.

(ix) *Chemical resistance*

Rubbers used for the lining of chemical plant, for the covers of certain conveyor belts and the inner lining of hose may operate in contact with a variety of oils, fats, greases, acids and alkalis. For many of these applications natural rubber has been replaced by one or other of the synthetics, but careful compounding is essential if the maximum life is to be obtained.

In order to test chemical resistance a test piece of the rubber is immersed in the liquid (concentration, temperature and time all being carefully controlled), and the resulting changes in volume and in mechanical properties are measured.

(x) *High temperature and low temperature properties*

Rocket research, high altitude flying and the increased interest in the Arctic and Antarctic regions have led to a demand for rubbers, which will retain their flexibility at temperatures well outwith the range commonly met with only a few years ago. It is not always sufficient simply to build a refrigerator or hot oven capable of taking the conventional test equipment, and special techniques are generally required.

(xi) *Electrical properties*

This is a specialised field. The electrical properties of polymers are mainly of interest to those engaged in the manufacture of cables and electrical insulation. However, the advent of electrically-conductive rubber and its use in situations where a build-up of static electricity could result in fire or explosion brings these properties to the attention of all rubber technicians.

(xii) *Determination of specific gravity*

The importance of specific gravity in compounding has been dealt with in Chapter X. Here are three methods of determining the specific gravity of solids.

Method 1. By flotation in solutions of known specific gravity.
This is an excellent method when large numbers of samples are to be
tested quickly, as for example in the routine testing of batches of
rubber stock. A series of solutions of known specific gravity (1·02 to
1·90 in steps of either 0·02 or 0·03) is prepared by adding water to a
concentrated master solution of zinc chloride, and checking the
specific gravity with a hydrometer until the correct figure is obtained.
For specific gravity below 1·00, mixtures of alcohol and water may be
used. The rubber sample is gripped in forceps, placed in the liquid,
air bubbles shaken off and the forceps removed. The sample may stay
at the level at which it was left when the forceps were removed, and if
so, it has the same specific gravity as the solution. It is more likely that
it will sink in one solution and float in the next solution in the series.
Its specific gravity therefore clearly lies between the specific gravity
values of these two solutions. With a little practice the specific gravity
may easily be read to the second decimal place. Solutions must be
kept covered when not in use, their specific gravity should be checked
regularly with a hydrometer and adjusted as necessary by adding either
water or master solution.

Method 2. By the 'Principle of Archimedes'. The 'Principle of
Archimedes' states that 'The apparent loss in weight of a body
immersed in a liquid is equal to the weight of liquid displaced'. If we
weigh a body in the ordinary way, i.e. in air, and then immerse it in
water and reweigh, we can subtract and find the apparent loss in
weight. By the 'Principle of Archimedes', this loss in weight is equal
to the weight of water displaced by the body. Since a body displaces
its own volume of liquid, this loss in weight must also be equal to the
weight of a volume of water equal to the volume of the body. We now
have the weight of the body and the weight of an equal volume of
water, and can therefore find the specific gravity which is, by definition,
the ratio

$$\frac{\text{weight of given volume of a substance}}{\text{weight of equal volume of water}}$$

Thus $\text{sp. gr.} = \dfrac{\text{weight of body in air}}{\text{wt. in air} - \text{wt. in water}}$

In making a specific gravity determination by this method, we use
a Students' Balance. The weight in air is obtained in the usual way,
but for the weight in water, a balance stool straddles the left-hand pan

M   C.R.T.

and supports a beaker of water in which the sample, hung from a thread, is immersed. The length of the thread and the size of the beaker must be such that, during the swinging of the balance arm, the sample is always fully immersed yet does not touch the bottom of the beaker.

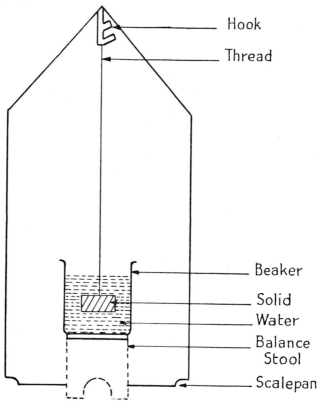

Hook

Thread

Beaker

Solid

Water

Balance
Stool

Scalepan

FIG. 51.   Weighing solid in liquid.

Method 3. By a Specific Gravity Balance. There are a number of special balances available, by which the sample can be weighed in air and then in water much more conveniently than on the chemical balance. The calculation

$$\frac{\text{wt. in air}}{\text{wt. in air} - \text{wt. in water}}$$

is done automatically and the specific gravity read directly from a scale. It is convenient to introduce here, methods for the determination of the specific gravity of liquids, although these are not directly concerned with the physical testing of rubber.

Method 1. By Specific Gravity Bottle. A specific gravity bottle is a small glass bottle, which contains an accurately known volume of liquid. It is provided with a glass stopper which fits exactly into the neck of the bottle. The specified volume, usually etched on the bottle, is obtained by filling the bottle with liquid, fitting the stopper and wiping off the overflow which issues from a tiny hole passing through the centre of the stopper.

The weight of the clean dry bottle and stopper is found. The bottle is filled with the liquid to be tested and the weight again taken. The bottle is emptied, cleaned if necessary, filled with water and reweighed. The weight of the empty bottle and stopper is subtracted in each case, and we then have the weight of a certain volume of the liquid and the weight of an equal volume of water, thus

$$\text{sp. gr.} = \frac{\text{weight of liquid}}{\text{weight of water}}.$$

Method 2. By Hydrometer. A hydrometer is a sealed glass tube with a weight (mercury or lead shot) at the bottom to make it float upright. It is floated in the liquid to be tested and the specific gravity is read off a scale at the point where the level of the liquid meets the stem of the hydrometer.

The principle of the hydrometer is based on the 'Law of Flotation' which states that floating bodies displace their own weight of fluid. The weight added to the base of the hydrometer determines the range of specific gravity it will cover — it sinks lower in fluids of lower specific gravity and rises higher in liquids of higher specific gravity.

In the rubber industry, hydrometers are used in determining the specific gravity of latex and in making up the solutions for the flotation method of measuring the specific gravity of rubber samples.

The technician may need to use a little ingenuity on occasion when asked to determine the specific gravity of an object which is too large for the above methods and from which samples may not be cut. The weight of the object can always be obtained and, if the object has a fairly regular shape, the volume can be calculated. If the shape of the object is such that its volume cannot be calculated, it can be found by displacement of water, by lowering the object into a suitable receptacle fitted with a siphon, and collecting and measuring the overflow water.

REFERENCES

DROGIN, I., Physical Testing. Charleston, West Virginia

Vanderbilt Rubber Handbook. 1948, New York, U.S.A.

BS 1673 *Methods of Testing Raw Rubber and Unvulcanised Compounded Rubber.*
Part 3: 1951, *Methods of Physical Testing;* Part 4: 1953, *Evaluation of Vulcanising Characteristics*

MORE, A. R., MORRELL, S. H. and PAYNE, A. R., The Wallace-Shawbury Curometer. *Rubber J. Int. Plast.* 1959, Vol. 136, 858–62

BS 1674: 1951. *Methods of Mixing and Vulcanising Rubber Test Compounds*

BS 903. *Methods of Testing Vulcanised Rubber.* Part A2: 1956, *Determination of Stress-Strain Properties;* Part A7: 1957, *Determination of Hardness*

BS 2719: 1956. *Pocket Type Rubber Hardness Meters*

SODEN, A. L., *A Practical Manual of Hardness Testing.* London

BUIST, J. M., *The Ageing and Weathering of Rubber.* Cambridge

CHAPTER XIV

FACTORIES ACTS, SAFETY AND HEALTH; WORK STUDY; MANAGEMENT

In this final chapter we will deal with certain syllabus subjects relating to industry in general, although emphasis will naturally be placed on those aspects having specific relevance to the rubber industry.

FACTORIES ACTS, SAFETY AND HEALTH

Until the Industrial Revolution, which commenced about the middle of the eighteenth century, most jobs in this country were associated with either textiles or agriculture. Goods were manufactured by the 'domestic' system, which means that the work was done in the homes of the operatives. The development of steam power, and its application to textile machinery, resulted in the establishment of gloomy and dangerous factories, many of which could justifiably be described as 'dark satanic mills'. Factories Acts have always largely concerned themselves with the safety of the worker, since the simple act of bringing people together in a factory, possibly equipped with power-driven machinery, greatly increases the risk of accident.

The initial legislation was enacted in 1802, but related only to textile factories. In 1832 the first Factory Inspectors were appointed, but safety provisions did not become law until 1844. Twenty years later non-textile factories were brought within the scope of the Acts, and in 1878 and 1901 further Acts of Parliament consolidated the existing laws and made a few additions. The Act of 1937, amended in 1948, represented a considerable advance and, although the legal requirements are now considered to have reached a reasonable standard, improvements are continually being made, the latest being embodied in the Factories Act of 1959. It must not be forgotten that these Acts are legal obligations, and it should be emphasised that any officer of a company may be guilty of an offence under the Act, if it is proved that a breach occurred as a result of his neglect, or with his consent or connivance. An officer of the company could be defined as anyone having any degree of responsibility.

165

The Factories Acts comprise 160 Sections dealing with health, safety and welfare, firstly for industry in general, then for particular industries. Other sections deal with the notification and investigation of accidents and industrial diseases, standards for the hours of employment of women and young persons, and finally, with interpretation, legal proceedings and administration. No one could be expected to know in detail all the provisions of the Acts, but the supervisor should have a knowledge of the general provisions and of any special details which relate to his own job. A brief but excellent *Guide to the Factories Acts* is available (see references at end of chapter) and a copy should be in the hands of everyone acting in any supervisory capacity.

In 1949 the National Joint Industrial Council for the Rubber Manufacturing Industry set up an Accident Prevention Committee, the object being to study (*a*) the legal requirements applicable to rubber factories, (*b*) all accidents occurring in rubber factories and (*c*) the risks peculiar to the industry. The Committee's work on (*a*) culminated in the publication of the above-mentioned *Guide to the Factories Acts*. Under (*b*) a survey and analysis of all accidents occurring between January 1950 and June 1952 established a pattern of the causes of accidents. This pattern has persisted to the present time, although the work of the Committee has brought about a welcome reduction in the accident frequency rate, from 1·57 to 1·00 in the space of ten years. The 'frequency rate' is the number of lost time accidents occurring for every 100,000 hours worked; a 'lost time accident' is one in which the injured person loses work beyond the shift in which the accident occurred.

Certain of the materials used in the rubber industry have inherent but known hazards for operatives — dermatitis from some powders and solvents, explosion and fire risk also from solvents and from materials in powder form. In this connection it is not generally realised that any material which will burn, even material which will not readily ignite in bulk form, may explode if sufficiently finely divided. Two risks of special importance to the rubber industry, two-roll mills and running nips, were considered by the Committee under item (*c*). The danger of trapping fingers in the nip of a two roll mill is obvious and fortunately this problem has now been largely solved. Other running nips pose a more difficult problem. By definition — 'a running nip is one where fabric or other similar material, being fed over, under or on to a roller, drum, box or cylinder, creates a nip with itself or with any other surface either moving or stationary'. Running nips can therefore be found in most rubber-working machinery — calenders and doubling machines, liner wrapping and unwrapping machines, spreading machines, etc. In spite of the difficulties in guarding such nips, a valuable report has been issued by the Committee giving causes and suggesting means of preventing running nip accidents.

Safety Mills

We will describe in some detail the safety features which U.K. rubber machinery manufacturers are now obliged to fit to all new mills. These features are referred to as the 'Lunn' principles, in recognition of the work on mill safety of R. W. Lunn of the Leyland & Birmingham Co. The Committee aimed at making it quite impossible for the operative's hands ever to approach the nip. Mills are set high, so that it is physically impossible for the average operator to get his hand near the nip under normal working conditions, provided, of course, he does not climb over the mill or perform some other unsafe act. In old mills a trench may be dug to lower the working position; new mills are set on a platform. An arrow is inscribed on the mil guides a short distance from the nip and the mill must carry a plate stating 'This mill is not safe for operatives who can reach beyond the safety limit. The arrow indicates the safety limit'. It is the duty of the supervisor to see that this provision is carried out although it may impede production by limiting certain operatives to certain mills. A sensitive safety bar is fitted just above the operative's waist level. A given pressure on this bar cuts off the power and applies a brake to the driving shaft. A grille of open pipe-work is fitted at the back of the mill to prevent the nip being reached from that position, but access to the roll is still possible to cut off material which has gone round the back roll. In those cases where cutting about of the rubber stock may be necessary on both rolls, an additional sensitive safety bar may be fitted at the back roll.

It must not be assumed that, prior to this work of the Safety Committee, open mills had no safety devices. Most had some arrangement of bars to prevent easy access to the nip and were provided with a quick stopping mechanism, operated by pulling on a wire or rod which ran the full width of the mill at both back and front. Of materials usually handled on roll mills rubber is unique, in that it may spring over on an operative's hand and seal up on itself, defying efforts to free the hand except by cutting away the rubber. Severe burning may also be suffered in such cases. In these and similar circumstances it was sometimes impossible for the operative himself to reach the tripping mechanism and he had to rely on another operative seeing his plight. The modern sensitive safety bar is so placed that, if a hand is trapped, the operative's own body will actuate the mechanism for stopping the mill.

Safety measures have not been finally defined for mills having rolls of 16 in. diameter and under, including laboratory type mills, as they are too small for the Lunn principles to apply fully. It will be found that there is a wide variety of guards and that their method of working varies also.

Technical and Non-technical Accidents

These terms are being used increasingly in Accident Prevention work. A 'technical' accident is one which requires the application of specialist knowledge in finding the solution, e.g. accidents on mills and at running nips. In a non-technical accident the solution is obvious and requires no specialist knowledge whatever. For example, accidents due to falling objects are 'non-technical', one solution is to insist that safety shoes be worn by all operatives handling heavy moulds or similar objects. In the rubber industry about 20% of all accidents are 'technical' and considerable success has been achieved in reducing them. However, it is unfortunate that little or no reduction has been made on the 80% of 'non-technical' accidents.

Dermatitis

The rubber industry uses many substances which may give rise to inflammation of the skin. The incidence of dermatitis is not, however, confined to the rubber industry; only about 3% of all cases of occupational dermatitis are to be found in the rubber and allied industries.

Certain people are allergic to dust and the only solution is to transfer them to some work where they will not encounter this trouble. Personal cleanliness is most important since unclean habits may predispose operatives to dermatitis, although not exactly causing it. An industrial dermatitis may be set up either by mechanical chafing or by chemical action. The skin may be broken by constant handling of rubbered fabric, and infection may result from an ingredient in the rubber. Irritation may be caused by acids used for pickling metal parts or by alkalis used as sweeteners in the cold cure process. Certain solvents remove the natural protective grease from the skin, leaving it coarse and dry and liable to crack. An obvious precaution is to use gloves or other protective clothing wherever possible. Since gloves destroy delicacy of touch, barrier creams may be employed; these are most conveniently supplied in dispensers, the operator rubbing a little of the cream into his hands before commencing work and again after the meal break.

To conclude this section here are a few basic safety rules intended mainly for the workshop and the laboratory.

1. Machines must not be operated until you have been instructed in their use; they must be operated only in the way you have been shown.

2. Safety devices fitted to mills, calenders, etc. must be checked for correct operation before work is started.

3. Knives and other cutting tools should be kept sharp and be used only as instructed; keep well clear of cutting edges.

4. Machinery in motion must be treated with extreme caution, especially in-running nips of mills and calenders, feed screws of extruders, etc. Although their speed is not high, keep clear of hydraulic press platens, whether the press is closing or opening. Loose coats, dangling shirt-sleeves and ties should be avoided.

5. Gloves should always be worn in handling hot moulds, mandrels, etc. but not for handling rubber stock on mill or calender. When moulding is finished, store hot moulds where they will not be handled inadvertently by another student, or mark the moulds 'HOT' in grease chalk.
Always allow ample time for the steam pressure in the curing pan to drop to zero and remove the lid very carefully until the contained steam has cleared.

6. Note the positions and method of operation of the fire extinguishers provided, and study carefully the action to be taken in case of fire.

7. As in the factory, good housekeeping in the workshop will contribute to your safety. Keep the floor free from water or oil, workbenches tidy, moulds stacked securely, tools in good condition, etc.

8. Avoid horseplay and general larking about. Unexpected loss of balance might lead to injury by falling, burning by contact with a hot platen or roll, or even loss of a finger or hand by trapping in a nip or wind-up.

It cannot be too strongly emphasised that the use of compressed air hoses, nozzles or needles for purposes other than those authorised is absolutely PROHIBITED.

9. Finally, if in doubt, ask your instructor, and do not proceed until you have had the point satisfactorily explained.

WORK STUDY

Work study is the study of work. This a simple yet all-embracing definition, since the work to be studied may not necessarily be in the factory. It may be in the office, in sport or even at home. Another definition might be 'common-sense applied to work'. The 'Training within Industry' (T.W.I.) scheme, started during World War II for rapid training of new workers, had this approach. Some of the questions that were posed during the analysis of an operation were — why is this job done?, why is it done at this stage?, why is it done in this way?

The term 'Work Study' includes all aspects of Method Study and Work Measurement. The aim of Work Study is to make a detailed analysis of each operation of a process, so that every unnecessary movement may be eliminated, that all necessary movements may be carried out in the most efficient way and then to standardise methods, equipment and working conditions. When all this has been done an assessment is made of the standard time in which the average operator can carry out the task.

Although it was not then called by its modern term, Work Study has been used for some fifty years, mainly in the engineering industry. It is now finding increasing application in all branches of industry and most large concerns have set up Work Study Departments. Smaller firms may have a Time Study, Standard Cost or Rate-fixing Section, but the term 'time study' is no longer favoured, since in the minds of the operatives it conjures up visions of black-coated staff using a stopwatch purely for the purpose of showing that the time taken for a job could be reduced drastically. This picture of Work Study is no longer true, since the relations between management and labour have improved considerably since the 1930's, and unjustifiable cutting of rates is no longer practised by reputable employers.

It must be admitted that Work Study has not yet been widely adopted by the medium and small size rubber manufacturing firms. This is evident from the data given in, for example, 'The Technologist in and about the Mill Room' by T. J. Daniel and W. C. Wake,

RABRM Bulletin, 1958, Vol. 12, 6, or by reference to 'Mill Room Productivity in the Rubber Industry' by the same authors, already mentioned in Chapter V. New projects are nowadays often on a vast scale, with a very high figure of capital invested per operative, and success or failure of the enterprise may turn on the accuracy of the figures obtained by Work Study.

Those students who are training for a post in which a working knowledge of Work Study will be required, should receive such instruction in the organisation itself. The references at the end of the chapter cater both for those requiring an elementary and an advanced knowledge of the subject.

MANAGEMENT

The craftsman or technician aiming at, say, shop manager status will receive instruction in management to suit the particular requirements of his own organisation. There are, however, a few points about Research and Development which are relevant at this stage.

'Why experiment? Our product is a good one, why not leave it alone?' are questions which might have been asked when early potters added the first decorative touches to their clay vessels, and they may still be heard in one form or another on the shop floor of the factory. The simple answer is that no manufacturing organisation can afford to rest on its laurels, the work of the Research and Development staff is essential to ensure *tomorrow's* wages for the operatives. The improved performance of the modern automobile — with faster acceleration, higher maximum speed, improved cornering properties and more efficient braking — has meant that tyre manufacturers have had to adopt new materials, new constructions and new techniques. The advent of cars which top the 100 m.p.h. mark has called for the development of tyres with a performance approaching that of racing tyres. Conveyor belts are required to carry heavier and more abrasive loads at higher speeds. The manufacturers of rubber footwear and clothing must be alive to the dictates of fashion, and innumerable other examples could be given. Production personnel, both staff and operatives, often express resentment when a succession of 'special' or 'non-standard' products is requested by the Technical Department. Such specials can certainly play havoc with piece-work rates and cherished production schedules, but they are not demanded just for sheer devilment.

Such factory applications, what might be termed 'applied' research, would eventually become ineffective were it not backed up by 'fundamental' research, i.e. the research which deals with such questions as the structure of the rubber molecule and how it may be modified, the precise manner in which rubber 'abrades' or wears away, how it perishes, how it can be made to adhere better to textile materials and a host of similar problems. In both fundamental and applied research, scientists are making full use of many recently developed instruments and techniques — the electron microscope, infra-red and ultra-violet rays, radio-active isotopes (ī'sō-tōps) and sound waves far above the limit of human hearing — 'ultrasonics'. So specialised has this work become that the modern tendency is to segregate it in large Research Departments, entirely separate from the production side of the organisation. Physically that may be desirable, but it tends to foster the idea that research is a thing quite apart from the daily round. Research is defined as 'diligent and careful inquiry or investigation' and is employed by operatives on the shop floor in gaining their intangible know-how, as well as by the learned boffin in the seclusion of his laboratory.

An excellent and very readable account of management for technical staff will be found in the papers presented at the I.R.I. Autumn Conference 1959 on 'Industrial Technical Organisation' (noted in the references), while a broader survey of the whole subject of management is given in Sir Frederic Hooper's book.

REFERENCES

A Guide to the Factories Acts. National Joint Industrial Council for the Rubber Manufacturing Industry

SMITH, S. F., Safety and Health in the Rubber Industry. *Proc. Inst. Rubber Ind.* 1958, Vol. 5, 44

PAGET, R. F., Safety in the Rubber Industry. *Proc. Inst. Rubber Ind.* 1957, Vol. 4, 147

Accident Prevention Manual. Dunlop Rubber Co. Ltd.

Safe Working on Horizontal Two Roll Mills. National Joint Industrial Council

Report on Causes of Running Nip Accidents and Suggested Means for the Prevention of Such Accidents. National Joint Industrial Council

Improvements in Safety Guards of Rubber Mills at RABRM. *RABRM Bulletin.* 1959, Vol. 13, 116

Safety and Health in Industry. Edinburgh and S.E. Scotland Industrial Safety Association

Outline of Work Study. British Institute of Management

LAMB, D. G. and WATSON, W. F., Safe Operation of Laboratory Mills. *Rubber Age*. 1960, Vol. 87, 485

CURRIE, R. M., *Work Study*. London

Industrial Technical Organisation. *Proc. Inst. Rubber Ind*. 1960, Vol. 7, 41

HOOPER, SIR FREDERICK, *Management Survey*. Pelican Books, A 474, Penguin Books, Middlesex

Supervisor's Handbook and Diary. Industrial Welfare Society, London

CALCULATIONS: GRAPHS

CALCULATIONS

In my contact with hundreds of students, I have found many with a distaste, almost amounting to a fear, of mathematics, probably resulting from the fact that the applications of mathematics had been insufficiently stressed at school. To any such students I would strongly recommend W. W. Sawyer's *Mathematician's Delight*. There are many excellent text books on elementary mathematics, several written with the student of technology in mind, but practically all that is required for the 'City and Guilds' syllabus will be found in the *Handbook of Workshop Calculations*. Both these books are noted in the references. We must now assume that the student has a working knowledge of the decimal system, metric units, percentages and simple algebraic notation. Indeed, mastery of these will solve the great majority of the day-to-day problems of the craftsman, technician and even junior technologist.

Specific Gravity; Cost per Pound; Volume Cost

The necessity for making such calculations has already been explained in Chapter X. Those students specialising in compounding should re-read Dr. Flint's 'Note for Students' referred to in that chapter.

Col. A	Col. B	Col. C	Col. D	Col. E	Col. F
Ingredient	*Weights*	*Sp. gr.*	*Volumes*	*Pence/lb.*	*Total pence*
Rubber	100·0	0·93	107·53	36·0	3600·0
Zinc oxide	5·0	5·57	0·90	12·0	60·0
Stearic acid	2·0	0·90	2·22	14·0	28·0
Sulphur	3·0	2·05	1·46	2·5	7·5
Accelerator	0·9	1·42	0·63	38·0	34·2
Carbon black	40·0	1·80	22·22	11·0	440·0
	150·9		134·96		4169·7

Note that the weights of the ingredients must be expressed in units and decimals of a unit, not in pounds and ounces.

Step 1. Divide the weight of each ingredient by its sp. gr. and enter the volumes so obtained in Col. D.

Step 2. Total Col. B to get the total weight of the batch.

Step 3. Total Col. D to get the total volume of the batch.

Step 4. Divide the total of Col. B by the total of Col. D to get the sp. gr. of the compound.

Step 5. Multiply the weight of each ingredient by its cost per lb. and enter in Col. F.

Step 6. Total Col. F to get the total cost of the batch.

Step 7. Divide the total of Col. F by the batch weight, to obtain the cost of the compound in pence per lb.

There are many ways of comparing the costs of compounds on a volume basis — some use the pound/volume, others the cost of a cubic inch or even the cost of a cubic foot.

Assuming we wish to find the cost of a cu. in., we would be given the weight of a cu. in. of water (0·036 lb.); multiplying this by the sp. gr. will give the weight of a cu. in. of the compound; multiplying again by the cost per lb. will give the cost of a cu. in.

We will not repeat the reasoning behind these operations — it should be clear from what has been said about specific gravity in Chapters X and XIII.

In the example given the sp. gr. is 1·118, the cost per lb. is 27·63d. and the cost per cu. in. is 1·112d.

Weight of Compound to Fill a Given Volume

If we are given or can calculate the volume of, say, a mould or an internal mixer we can easily find the weight of a compound of known sp. gr. which will occupy this volume. We simply multiply 0·036 lb. (the weight of a cu. in. of water) by the sp. gr. to get the weight of a cu. in. of the compound, and multiply again by the desired volume in cu. in.

This statement can be expressed much more compactly if we use what is termed a mathematical 'formula'. In this, letters are used to denote quantities, and, provided we obey the rules of elementary algebra, replacing the letters by the quantities they represent in any particular problem and working out the result is quite a simple operation. In fact the formula *is* the answer, but care is necessary in keeping the units right, e.g. if one part of the problem is in cu. ft. and another in cu. in. both must be brought to the same basis.

The volume problem above may be written

$$W = V \times G \times 0.036$$

where W = weight to fill mould in lb.

V = volume of mould in cu. in.

G = sp. gr. of compound.

If the mould were rectangular of length l, breadth b and depth d, all in inches

then $V = l \times b \times d$ or simply lbd,

giving $W = lbdG \; 0.036$ or $0.036 \; lbdG$

the second form avoiding possible misreading.

Percentages

A percentage is simply a rate per hundred units. When written out thus 'per cent.' there is usually a full stop after the cent. to indicate that it is an abbreviation of *centum*, the Latin word for hundred. The sign for 'per cent.' is %, which contains the two zeros of 100 and the numeral 1 as the middle bar.

If we express the numbers of scrap products made in relation to 100 units produced, we then have a basis for comparing results over a shift, a day or any other period as required.

In Chapter IX we gave two ways of writing the formula for a rubber compound, (*a*) based on 100 parts of rubber hydrocarbon (PHR), and (*b*) based on a total batch weight of 100, i.e. each ingredient is given as a percentage of the total. If you compare these now, you will see that, to correspond with the change in total weight from 152·1 to 100·0, the weight of every ingredient in (*a*) has been changed in the ratio 100·0/152·1. It is customary to use a Latin phrase for this operation: we say that the ingredient weights have been changed 'pro rata', or even that they have been 'pro-rated' although the verb is not yet accepted as good English.

It should be noted that masterbatches are usually referred to on a percentage basis, a 10% masterbatch containing 10% of the ingredient and 90% of rubber. Given the weight of the ingredient required in the finished compound and the percentage strength of the masterbatch, it is simple to calculate the weight of masterbatch needed.

$$\text{Weight of } M/b \text{ required} = \frac{\text{Weight of ingredient} \times 100}{\% \text{ of ingredient in } M/b}$$

Remember to deduct from the raw or 'free' rubber in the formula, the weight of rubber added as masterbatch. The position may be complicated by the presence of small quantities of other ingredients in the masterbatch, but the principle of the calculation is the same.

The number 100 is often used to indicate a standard level of price, quality, performance, etc. The 120 level tyre sells at 20% more than the standard tyre; an 80 level rubber compound would be only 80% as good as the standard in some particular property; a rating of 150 in belting performance indicates that it has lasted half as long again as the standard quality.

In making percentage and rating calculations it is useful to remember, especially for slide rule work, that adding 25% to a number is the same as multiplying the number by 1·25.

Hydraulic Power

The construction of the hydraulic press has been described in Chapter VIII, but here is a short summary. A press is simply a squeezing device; a hydraulic press is one in which the squeezing is done by means of a liquid under pressure (pressure is just a force pushing against a surface); the liquid usually employed is water, hence the name 'hydraulic'. When a liquid is under pressure, the pressure is exerted equally in all directions and, since liquids are practically incompressible, we have a convenient means of transmitting pressure from one point to another.

The capacity of a press is stated in tons, and is calculated by finding the area of the ram, multiplying it by the hydraulic pressure and converting to tons.

Where R is the radius (half the diameter) of the ram in inches, P the hydraulic pressure in p.s.i. and T the press tonnage, the formula would be

$$T = \frac{\pi R^2 P}{2240}$$

Given T and P we can calculate R, given T and R we can find P.

For ordinary moulding a minimum pressure of about 1,250 lb. is required on every square inch of mould surface. The above formula may be used to find if a press has sufficient tonnage for the area of the moulding it is producing. When an inflatable product, such as a tyre curing bag, is being cured in a hydraulic press, the calculation of ram diameter should include a safety factor, since a heavy draw on the hydraulic system may result in the pressure of the inflation medium,

N   C.R.T.

air or steam, overcoming the ram pressure and permitting the mould to open, possibly with disastrous results.

This same calculation may be applied to any similar system, e.g. the air-operated ram of an internal mixing machine.

Tensile Strength

In Chapter XIII it was explained that the stress on a tensile test sample is calculated as the load per unit area of the original (un-stretched) sample cross-section. For calculation of the tensile strength we must know the width and thickness of the test strip and the load necessary to break it, or to stretch it to intermediate elongations if we are interested in the modulus values.

If L is the load in lb., W the sample width in in., G the sample thickness in in. and TS the tensile strength in p.s.i., then

$$TS = \frac{L}{W \times G}$$

A standard sample width is $\frac{1}{4}$ in. and, as it is common to measure the sample thickness in thousandths of an inch and call it the 'gauge', the formula then becomes

$$TS = L \left/ \left(\frac{1}{4} \times \frac{G}{1000} \right) \right. = L \times \frac{4000}{G}$$

Most modern tensile testers either draw the stress/strain curve auto-matically, or compensate for the thickness of the test-piece and indicate the stress in p.s.i. However, if it is necessary to go back to first principles, you would read the loads in lb. corresponding to each 100% increase in elongation (strain), work out the factor $4000/G$, multiply it by each load in turn and so obtain the corresponding stresses.

GRAPHS

A graph (from the Greek word *graphein* — to write) is a pictorial way of representing the relationship between two, or sometimes more, properties. A graph can summarise neatly the information contained in long tables of figures. It can show in what direction a property is tending and enables us to read off values which are not easily found from the original data.

Graphs are drawn on some form of squared paper, the ruling of the squares making it easy to 'plot the points'. An ordinary graph has two 'axes' (plural of 'axis') at right angles to one another, the horizontal, or x, axis and the vertical, or y, axis. The point on the bottom left of the graph where the two axes meet is termed the 'origin'.

Graphs may be extremely complicated, but we are concerned only with the following, which are quite straightforward (a) the relationship between the load applied to a rubber sample and the elongation produced by that load (the stress/strain curve); (b) the relationship between time of cure and the physical properties of a compound; (c) variation in plasticity value with temperature of mastication; (d) representation of the variations of scrap percentage of a product over a period of time. Graph (d) differs from the first three in that it is a graph of 'statistics', the others being graphs of 'functions'. In mathematics one quantity is said to be a function of another if a change in one produces a change in the other. In (a) a change of load changes the elongation; in (b) a change in the time of cure produces a change in physical properties; in (c) a change in the temperature at which mastication is carried out changes the plasticity. Although the term 'statistics' has the broad meaning of 'the classification, tabulation and study of numerical facts' we are here concerned with the simpler meaning of 'numerical facts' only. In (d) the scrap percentage is not a function of time — it might be said to depend on it, but not in the mathematical sense, a point we will clarify in Appendix B.

In constructing a graph we proceed as follows:

Step 1. Choose the size of squared paper appropriate to the purpose of the graph, for example a large size may be required for wall display. The most suitable ruling for our work is inches and tenths of an inch.

Step 2. Choose which property is to be shown on the vertical axis and which on the horizontal. This is a matter sometimes of convenience and sometimes of convention, for instance it is customary to draw stress/strain curves with the load on the vertical axis and the elongation on the horizontal axis. Mark the axes with the property to be shown and the units in which it is measured. Add a title, date and any other distinguishing information.

Step 3. Choose a scale appropriate to the range of values of the data given, and mark off the axes in equal divisions. Avoid a scale which divides an inch into 3 or its multiples; keep to 5, 4 or 2 divisions.

Step 4. Plot the points. This entails marking a point with a cross (X)

or encircled dot (⊙) at the intersection of two imaginary lines drawn at right angles to the axes, at distances corresponding to the values stated as equivalent in the data. This sounds complicated but Fig. 53 should clarify it.

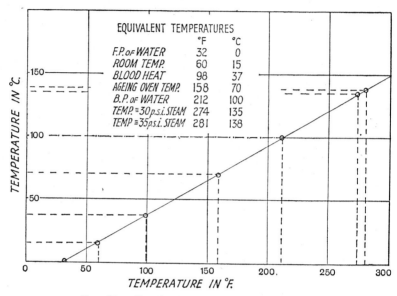

Fig. 53.   Graph of Centigrade and Fahrenheit
equivalent temperatures.

Step 5. Join up the points so obtained. Graphs of functions should give (within the limits of experimental error) either a straight line or a smooth curve. In graphs of statistics the points should be joined up with straight lines and no attempt made to 'smooth' out the variations (there are ways of finding the trend of such graphs, but they are beyond the scope of this text).

Conversion of Temperature Scales

Most factory equipment is based on the Fahrenheit scale of temperature measurement, but some new equipment may use the Centigrade system. It is thus necessary to know how each scale is constructed, and how temperatures on one scale may be converted to the other.

The Fahrenheit (F) scale is named after its originator. It is unfortunate that in his experiments with freezing mixtures Fahrenheit thought he had reached the lowest possible temperature attainable, which he took as his zero or 0° F. Fahrenheit chose the length of his divisions so that 32° F became the temperature at which water freezes, and made a difference of 180 divisions between the freezing and boiling points of water, making the latter 212° F. Note that it is becoming increasingly common to omit the degree sign when quoting temperatures, e.g. 212 F instead of 212° F.

The Centigrade system is more logical. The name means a scale made up of 100 steps or degrees (from the Latin, *centum* — and *gradus* — step). This scale is now officially referred to by the name of its inventor, Celsius. There are 100 divisions between the freezing point and boiling point of water, which are 0° C and 100° C respectively on this scale.

In converting temperatures from one scale to the other, it is best not to rely on memorising a formula, but to draw or picture in the mind's eye a diagram as in Fig. 54. We see that 100 C divisions are equal to 180 F divisions, or 5 C divs. equal 9 F divs. and similarly 9 F divs. equal 5 C divs. Conversion would be perfectly straightforward, if it were not for the fact that this relationship is directly true only between the lower and upper fixed points. When going from C to F we therefore multiply by $\frac{9}{5}$ and then add 32. Going from F to C, we first subtract 32 and then multiply by $\frac{5}{9}$. If in doubt, remember the

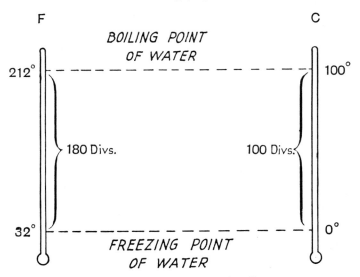

FIG. 54.   Temperature conversion diagram.

equivalence of 100° C and 212° F and ask yourself how to convert from one to the other. Since $\frac{9}{5}$ is equal to 1·8 a neat way of converting from C to F is thus,

$$
\begin{array}{r}
60 \text{ C} \\
1{\cdot}8 \\
\hline
480 \\
60 \\
32 \\
\hline
140{\cdot}0
\end{array}
$$

but watch that you add the 32 in the correct position in relation to the decimal point.

A conversion method useful particularly to those who have not learned any other, is the +40 −40 technique. No matter from which scale we wish to covert, the first operation is to add 40 and the third operation is to subtract 40. The second operation is to multiply by $\frac{9}{5}$ when going from C to F and to multiply by $\frac{5}{9}$ when going from F to C. Remembering which multiplier to use is quite easy, since, for the same temperature, the F reading is, with a few exceptions, numerically greater than the C reading. The operations may be tabulated thus

$$C, +40, \times \tfrac{9}{5}, -40, F$$
$$F, +40, \times \tfrac{5}{9}, -40, C$$

Tables of equivalent temperatures are to be found in handbooks, etc. of all technologies where temperature conversions may be needed.

Miscellaneous

The technician who is assigned to, say, process control duties, will find innumerable applications for simple mathematics, in translating the product design specification into shop floor terms. If the working specification is accurate, time, money and effort can all be saved. It often happens that a formula developed for one particular process may be applied in many other ways. Here is just one example: a formula expressing the relationship between the outside diameter of a roll of sheet rubber, belting or similar material and the length contained in the roll. Where L is the yardage, G the thickness of the material in inches, D and d the outside diameters of roll and box (shell) respectively, also in inches,

then
$$L = \frac{0 \cdot 0218 \, (D^2 - d^2)}{G}$$

or
$$D = 2 \sqrt{\frac{36GL}{\pi} + r^2}$$

In the second case it is more convenient to use the radius of the shell, r in. This formula in either of its forms will save a great deal of trial and error, since it is frequently more convenient to measure the outside diameter of a roll rather than the yardage it contains. A small correction may be necessary due to deformation of the rubber, each case being treated individually.

Engineering Drawing

The craftsman and technician requires to have some knowledge of the methods employed and the signs used in making simple engineering drawings. He may be asked to decide if a design for a mould, existing only in drawing form, will fit a particular press, or he may have to calculate how much rubber stock he will require to check the volume and produce the first moulding.

Every engineering job is first set down on paper and the drawing is prepared showing all the relevant information, so that the component can be manufactured without further reference to any other data.

All that the City and Guilds student needs to know of engineering drawing will be found in the two books listed in the references.

REFERENCES

Handbook of Workshop Calculations. H.M.S.O., London

SAWYER, W. W., *Mathematician's Delight.* Pelican Books, A 121, Penguin Books, Middlesex

Vanderbilt Rubber Handbook, 1958, New York, U.S.A., pp. 529–48

BAKER, C. C. T., *Practical Mathematics.* Vol. I, London

LONGLAND, W., *How to Read Workshop Drawings.* London

BS 308A: 1958. *Engineering Drawing Practice.* Abridged edition for students, British Standards Institution, London

FACTORY PROBLEMS: REPORT WRITING: TECHNICAL INFORMATION

In this section we will outline the method of attacking day-to-day problems, give some guidance in writing the report which should follow the solution of a problem, and conclude by indicating some sources of technical information.

FACTORY PROBLEMS

The Rubber and Plastics Research Association of Great Britain (RAPRA) has classified the inquiries received from member firms as follows: examination or evaluation of raw materials; design of mixings; processing troubles; utilisation of scrap; tests on finished products; failures in service.

The approach to any of these will, of course, depend on the size of the factory and the facilities available. The small factory, with perhaps only one technical assistant and the minimum of test equipment, might have to refer all problems to the RAPRA or request assistance from a material supplier. The largest organisations, most of which now comprise of 'Groups' of smaller firms, would rarely require outside help. Their size permits the provision and full utilisation of control laboratories, product test laboratories and centres for research, all equipped with the latest test apparatus. I consider, however, that the technical assistant is best served in the medium-sized factory where he is neither frustrated by lack of essential equipment nor by the detached attitude sometimes adopted by scientists who have spent little, if any, time on the shop floor.

In Chapter XIII we dealt very briefly with the examination of raw materials, tests on finished products and failures in service. In Chapter V we discussed the design of mixings to suit both customers' requirements and the requirements of processing. Chapter VII gave the sources of basic mixings for all products, and stressed the point that the art of the compounder lay in making those slight modifications necessary to keep processing troubles to a minimum. Chapter

184

VII also mentioned the utilisation of uncured scrap, while the re-claiming of cured scrap and the use of rubber crumb were noted in Chapters IX and X respectively. Chapter VII considers in great detail all the manifestations of the scorch problem, which heads the list of processing troubles. Reference to Table IV in that chapter should give the technician at least a starting point in tracking down almost any processing problem.

'Trouble-shooting' is one of the functions of what is usually termed the 'process control' section of the Technical Department. Once Sales have received management approval of what is to be made and in what types and sizes, Product Design takes over and draws up the product specification. This goes to Process Development who translate the design drawings into satisfactory prototypes and finalise the product specification for the factory. At this stage Process Control comes into the picture and is responsible for all technical aspects of getting the maximum production consistent with an acceptable quality level. This Technical Department set-up applies to medium and large organisations, although the names may differ somewhat, but in the small firm all these technical functions may be carried out by the 'Lab' perhaps staffed by only one 'chemist' and an assistant.

Economic production demands that the percentage of scrap and defective goods be kept to a minimum. The management will probably set a target figure, best displayed as a bold line in a distinctive colour on the graphs of scrap and defects, which should be made out by Process Control personnel. When we talked about graphs in Appendix A, the point was made that in one sense such defect graphs may de-pend on time, since the management will expect, as time goes on, that the actual defect line will draw closer to the target. When this happens it will probably result in a further lowering of the target, a perfectly legitimate procedure which should not be resented but rather re-garded as a challenge. Here are some hints for improving, in particular, the defective product position, although a similar approach could well be used to any factory problem.

First we must get the facts and then attempt to establish a pattern. Getting the facts is not always easy and quite a bit of detective work may be involved. Supervision of special lots will probably be neces-sary, with a check being kept on all conditions of operation — time, temperature, pressure, etc. Faulty instruments should not be over-looked. Once we know what is actually happening, we can then deter-mine if there has been any departure from the process laid down when the prototype product was made. However small the factory, it is important to have written records of how the manufacturing process is carried out. Apart from the obvious use in getting manufacture started, such records are needed for planning, costing, work study and training of new supervisors and operatives. The facts established, we now seek a pattern in the defect picture by working backwards from the product itself to the raw materials of which it is composed.

TABLE VIII

Stage of Manufacture	Questions to be asked
Product	What size, type, pattern; location of defect.
Curing	What curing process, curing schedule, unit, position in the unit, department, shift, gang, operator. What time of occurrence of defect in relation to — meal break, start or finish of shift, start or finish of week. Variation in services — steam, air, water, hydraulic or electrical power.
Storage	What are conditions of storage — temperature, humidity, exposure to sunlight. What length of time in storage, are products used in rotation, is distortion occurring.
Product Assembly	What is the relationship of the defect area to its position in the uncured product. Is the assembly to design requirements — dimensions, stepping of components.
Component Assembly and Raw Materials	Are dimensions to design. Is the defect associated with particular compounds, perhaps using the same polymer or compounding ingredient. Is a particular textile involved.
Ancillary Materials	Is the defect attributable to the use of faulty or incorrect quantities of solvents, solutions, mould dopes, dusting agents, linings, etc.
Process	Have there been any recent changes in labour, supervision or in the authorised method of manufacture.

This is a formidable list, but it is amazing how quickly it can be tackled, especially if the process control assistant has a routine of checking certain key-points in the shop where departures from set standards are likely to give trouble at later stages of manufacture. Indeed it has been said that the value of a technical assistant varies inversely as the number of times his help has to be called for, in other words he knows at what points to exercise extremely tight control, thus anticipating later trouble. Since modern management does not take kindly to interruptions in production, the technical assistant nowadays must often solve problems while production is still continuing. However, if he uses the approach outlined here and keeps a careful record of his findings, his problems should not be insuperable. The student will find it an instructive exercise to study Table VIII in detail and satisfy himself that he understands the reason behind each question.

Report Writing

The writing of reports is one aspect of 'communications', so named since its object is to communicate information from one mind to another. The simple shop floor instruction given by word of mouth, the annual company report of the organisation, or the intricate report on the proposed development, manufacture and marketing of a new material or product, are all examples of 'communications'.

We have already indicated that an important final step in the solution of a problem is a written report. Such a report will almost certainly be requested by a superior, but in any case the technician should record what has been done, so that neither he himself nor his successor need start from scratch, if the particular problem or one of a similar nature should recur. If for record purposes only, the report may employ a certain amount of factory and shop floor 'jargon', but if the report is for use outside the department (or for examination purposes) greater precision in expression is necessary. 'Jargon' may be defined in this context as technical phraseology understood inside a particular industry or branch of industry but unintelligible to outsiders. For example, 'the introduction of SBR latex into the dope resulted in severe plucking due to loss of green stick' might just be understood by some students, but would hardly be acceptable to higher management and would be severely criticised by an examiner. The statement should be rephrased and amplified thus, 'The loss of uncured rubber/textile adhesion, due to the introduction of a proportion of SBR latex into the fabric dip solution, has meant that the coating could easily be pulled off the fabric during the assembly operation.'

For many years I have myself used, and have instructed students in, the report writing technique recommended by F. C. Jennings in his paper on 'Presentation of Technical Information' (see references). Since this approach cannot be improved on, I quote, by permission of Mr. Jennings. "Your report will most likely be addressed to two main types of reader: the specialist in the same field, and the busy executive who wants to gather its general drift quickly and perhaps to be able to act on it when he has related your conclusions to other work on hand. There may be others also with different degrees of interest between these two, but, it is often possible for one report to serve all of them in this way.

"Write it so that only the specialist needs to read it all the way through. To be more precise, write it so that the ideas form a sequence from the more general to the more particular.

"First, there is the *title*. Make it short but comprehensive, bold and attractive. Then write an *introduction* or brief preface, which may be historical or argumentative, designed to take the busy man on a brief tour of the whole problem so that he can see the origin and extent of the work. Follow this at once by your *conclusions* and state any recommended action. This is the 'meat' of your report and must be well-cooked, if not pre-digested, so that the reader can make a satisfying meal easily and palatably. Go on next to a description of the *methods* of testing and the apparatus used; then give the *results*, discuss their meaning and significance, restate your conclusions, and suggest the lines for further work, if desirable.

"This might be called the 'TICMR' scheme: Title, Introduction, Conclusions, Methods, Results. Its advantage is that the busy man at his desk needs to read only the TIC part, by far the smallest part, to get from it what he wants, while your fellow-expert can read right through to the end, knowing from quite near the beginning what you are aiming at and so being able to follow your arguments and lines of thought much more readily."

When your report is completed (do not forget the date) set it aside until, say, the next day. On rereading it, keep asking yourself what meaning you wish each sentence to convey to the reader and make sure that what you have actually said does convey this meaning, without any possibility of misinterpretation. Finally, check your punctuation, add the circulation, that is the list of names of those who are to receive the report, and send your report for typing. Always check the typescript before you finally append your signature, in case there have been any typing errors.

Technical Information

During my years of teaching I have often had to restrain the eager student who wants to buy *all* the technical books and read *all* the technical information available on his subject. I have been at pains to point out that he must be selective in his reading; some guidance is given in Appendix E. Here I wish to show the student where to find information when it is needed.

Provided the student is employed by a member firm of the RAPRA, he should have no difficulties in obtaining information. Any published information relating to rubber, rubber-like materials, plastics and ancillary materials used in association with these can be speedily traced by the RAPRA Information Service. Indeed there is little published about rubber, technical or commercial, that is not reported or made available to members. The monthly publication *Rubber Abstracts* contains, in the form of short digests, the essence of some 1,600 articles in periodicals, catalogues, patents, pamphlets, etc. The RAPRA Library is believed to be the most complete and comprehensive in its particular subject in the whole world. A recent survey of the activities of the RAPRA sevice is given in 'Rubber and Plastics Information Service' noted in the references.

The late T. R. Dawson, who founded the RAPRA Library and Intelligence Division, examined all the existing systems of classifying scientific literature, found none entirely suitable for his purpose and devised one of his own. This system, now known by the initials ICCRI (International Committee for the Classification of Rubber Information), has, with very slight modification been used to classify all new developments in rubber science and technology. On this most elegant system is based the RAPRA reputation for speedy answering of inquiries. All incoming material is 'abstracted', the short summaries are entered on cards, which are then classified according to subject matter. A short description of the system will be found in 'Class numbers for I.R.I. Papers' *Trans. Inst. Rubber Ind.*, 1958, Vol. 34, 1. Since this efficient service is available to the rubber industry, or rather to RAPRA members, it might be thought that it would not be necessary for individual organisations to operate their own information services. This is dealt with in Mr. G. A. Shires's 'Technical Information Service in the Rubber Industry' (see references), where it is pointed out that, however diligent the RAPRA abstractors, they cannot answer the question posed by the individual firm, 'What is there in it for *us*?' In this connection it is useful to remember that the author of a technical paper cannot always indicate in the necessarily short title the full scope of his work; although the title might convey that 'there is little in it for *him*', the diligent reader will often be rewarded with little gems of information by glancing at what might appear unpromising material. A case in point is a paper by C. E. Webb 'Developments in the Technology of the Direct Moulded Footwear Process' *Proc. Inst. Rubber Ind.*, 1960, Vol. 7, 95, which contains much of general interest in the compounding of rubber for short cures at high temperatures.

The student who intends to specialise in some technical capacity would be well advised to join the Institution of the Rubber Industry and receive the bi-monthly *Transactions* and *Proceedings*. These are bound as one, the *Transactions* catering more for the scientist, the *Proceedings* for the technologist. The *Annual Report on the Progress of Rubber Technology*, also issued by the Institution, is a critical review of the year's progress compiled by experts in their own particular fields. In Appendix E a reading List will supplement this brief introduction to information on rubber.

REFERENCES

Vanderbilt Rubber Handbook. 1948, New York, U.S.A., pp. 537–40

PANZETTA, F. M., General Factory Problems. *India Rubber Journal*. 1952, Vol. 122, 833

EVANS, B. B., Pilot Scale to Production. *Proc. Inst. Rubber Ind*. 1957, Vol. 4, 21

Applications of Science in Rubber Technology. Imperical Chemical Industries, Dyestuffs Division, Manchester

KAPP, R. O., *Presentation of Technical Information*. London

JENNINGS, F. C., Presentation of Technical Information. *Trans. Inst. Rubber Ind*. (Supplement) 1951, Vol. 27, No. 5

SHIRES, G. A., Technical Information Service in the Rubber Industry. *Trans. Inst. Rubber Ind*. 1948, Vol. 24, 120

ANON., Searching the Literature for Information on Rubber. *Rubber Journal*. 1956, Vol. 131, 749

FIG. 55. "We did it Bellamy — we certainly fixed that one-and-a-half inch extruder automatic take off."

APPENDIX C

INSTRUMENTATION AND AUTOMATIC CONTROL

In the course of this text we have often described processes in which specified conditions of time, temperature and pressure have to be maintained. Now we must look at the means by which such conditions are indicated, recorded and controlled.

When curing times were measured in hours rather than minutes, wide variations in the curing conditions were permissible without detracting from the quality level acceptable at that period. A heavy sulphur 'bloom' (a surface coating of that sulphur which has not combined with the rubber), quite unacceptable nowadays, was then regarded as desirable. As compounding developed and curing times were reduced, there was a corresponding development in the applications of instrumentation, for indicating and recording time, temperature, air and hydraulic pressures, etc., and of automatic control which maintains the specified conditions without the attention of the operative. Of all industrial processes, the vulcanisation of rubber is one of the most highly instrumented. Curing conditions must be accurately maintained since the rate of cure follows a general chemical law in that it is approximately doubled for every 18 F degrees increase in temperature, and conversely, is halved for every 18 F degrees drop in temperature.

There are three main stages in the development of automatic control. In the first stage a measure of the condition is recorded on an indicator such as a thermometer or pressure gauge, which must be observed by an operative, who then performs some manual act to correct the condition if the indicator reading does not tally with the specified figure. The obvious disadvantages of this method are the reliance placed on the human element and the fact that the conditions are known only at the moment of reading the instrument. In the second stage we use some means of making a continuous record of the conditions, thus providing a check on the operative, and, since the extent of any variation can be seen, this enables a correction to be made before the completion of the process, with a possible saving of scrap and defective products. The third stage is the fully automatic operation of a specified schedule of time, temperature and pressure, the only manual intervention being the pushing of a button to start the cycle. In this connection we will refrain from using the word 'automation', since the rubber industry has not yet adopted, and may never fully adopt, the concepts which the engineer understands by the term, i.e. the removal of human operatives from a process or machine, the automatic operation of the machine, which also controls the level of its own output, recognises faulty operation and is capable of self-correction.

Measurement of Time and Speed

A variety of interval timers is available, operated either electrically or by clockwork for indicating a length of time. Electrical operation is most convenient but clockwork is still common for the driving mechanism of recorder charts. Interval timers are usually provided with some means of calling the operator's attention — the flashing of a light or the ringing of a bell. The technician should have the use of an accurate stop-watch as a check on all interval timers, since maladjustment may occur. A stop-watch is also useful for checking the speeds of mill rolls, slow running conveyor belts, etc., the time of travel for a given distance being noted. For speeds of faster belts and of shafting we use an instrument called a 'tachometer' (takom'-eter), the spindle of which is provided with a small wheel for taking belt speeds and a spiked end for shaft speeds. Tachometers read directly in yards or feet per minute and in revolutions per minute (r.p.m.).

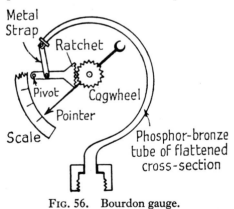

FIG. 56.　Bourdon gauge.

Measurement of Pressure or Vacuum

This is usually done by a 'Bourdon' type of gauge. The pressure or vacuum source is connected to a steel tube of elliptical cross-section, bent to a semi-circular shape or coiled up in spiral form. The tube winds up or unwinds under pressure changes, and this twisting action of the Bourdon tube actuates, through a rack and pinion movement, a pointer which moves over a graduated circular scale (Fig. 56). Adjustable electrical contacts may be fitted to the face of the gauge for operation of a warning device or of a control system.

Measurement of Thickness

The measurement of the thickness of material in process may be done by a modified type of dial thickness gauge, in which the standard pressure foot and anvil have been replaced by small rollers which run on the material. It is not very convenient or accurate and therefore a continuous-indicating thickness meter of the 'Schuster' type is often preferred. This instrument measures the space between the calender bowl and a roller which runs on the rubber film or coated fabric. It is electro-magnetic in operation and does not read absolute thickness but indicates any departure from a set thickness. This gauge may also be worked in conjunction with a control unit which opens or closes the calender nip as the rubber thickness decreases or increases respectively.

Radio-active isotopes are now being employed in non-contacting thickness gauges. Beta rays are directed through the rubber or coated fabric, and the reduction in intensity of the rays is measured, thus indicating the thickness of the material.

Measurement of Weight

Accurate weighing is of extreme importance in the rubber industry and in all weighing operations it is important to choose a scale of suitable capacity — it is folly, for example, to attempt to weigh accurately 0·5 lb. of an ingredient or masterbatch on a scale with a capacity of 250 lb. For stationary weighing a type of springless dial scale is common, dead weight balances being used for smaller quantities. The steelyard type of weighbridge is still universally used, but for storage tanks and bins a modern method of weighing is to use a 'load cell', a device which indicates the weight by the change in electrical resistance of a strain gauge. Continuous weighing may be

o   C.R.T.

done by passing the material (extruded sections, calendered sheet or fabric) on a conveyor belt over a series of rollers which are connected to a weighing scale. An appropriate adjustment, of course, is made for the weight of the belt itself.

Heat Transmission

Since heat is so extensively employed in the curing process we must discuss briefly how heat is transmitted from one point to another. The student should re-read Chapter VIII at this stage and be very clear as to the distinction between heat and temperature.

There are three ways by which heat is transmitted, viz., conduction, convection and radiation.

In conduction of heat there is actual contact between the heat source and the body to which the heat is being given, e.g. a hot soldering bolt supplies heat by direct contact with the solder.

In convection of heat, a fluid medium (gas or liquid) passes over the heat source and so carries the heat elsewhere. Hot water 'radiators' for room heating operate mainly by convection, the heated air above the radiator rising and drawing in colder air from the room.

In radiation, the heat is transmitted from the source to the body being heated, in straight lines similar to the radiation of light.

We may easily remember these three methods of heat transmission if we visualise one of the new electric convector heaters which has also a one-bar radiator element. If we touch the top metal part of the heater we will receive heat by conduction; if we hold our hands near the louvres at the top, we will receive heat by convection — from the current of air which has been warmed as it passes over an electrical element in the base; if we hold our hands in front of the glowing spiral of wire (through which a current of electricity is passing) we will be heated by radiation.

Since the production of heat energy is costly (steam from coal or oil, electricity from a supply authority) it is important to prevent as far as possible any loss of heat by conduction, convection or radiation, from any heated surface. This is done by covering such areas, pipes, tanks, etc., by a layer of a poor heat conductor. This not only saves fuel, but also keeps the temperature of a workshop reasonable and prevents burning injuries resulting from contact with the hot surfaces. Such 'lagging' materials, as they are called, should of course be very poor conductors of heat, they should be non-combustible, easily applied and long lasting. Where the equipment may have to be taken apart for cleaning or the replacement of gaskets, etc., the lagging should preferably be in jacket form. For domestic purposes, felt or flannel are cheap and useful lagging materials, but for larger installations, asbestos fibre mixed into plaster form or made up into blankets or coils is preferred. In refrigeration systems it is important to keep heat out, and cork is often employed. More expensive but much more efficient is a product of the rubber industry — expanded ebonite.

Steam Traps

To maintain correct curing conditions in steam-heated vulcanising equipment, it is important that all condensate be removed as soon as it is formed. 'Condensate' is the name given to the water formed when steam has lost its heat (either by doing the work expected of it or by unwanted radiation) and has returned to the liquid state. If steps are not taken to remove condensate regularly, the water will build up in the bottoms of autoclaves, lower surfaces of press platens, etc., and result in 'waterlogging' of the equipment with consequent undercure of the product. Indeed, the efficiency of any steam-heated plant depends ultimately on the efficiency of the condensate removal system.

Condensate may be discharged in several ways. One of the crudest ways is simply to open a valve at intervals and permit the live steam to blow the water out, but in general some form of steam trap is employed. This is a device which operates automatically, it opens to discharge condensate and closes when live steam reaches it. Keeping the system clear of condensate in this way ensures that the heating efficiency is kept at a high level and there is no loss of heat by blowing off live steam.

Steam traps are of two main types — mechanical and thermostatic. In the mechanical type, the condensate builds up in the body of the trap, raising a float which finally operates a lever and opens a valve through which the condensate is discharged. The float may be a bucket-shaped vessel, or a hollow ball similar to that used in the domestic water supply cistern. In the thermostatic type of trap, the drop in temperature due to the entry of condensate causes the thermostatic element to contract and open a valve through which the water passes. When live steam again enters, the higher temperature expands the element and closes the valve.

Fig. 57 shows a typical mechanical trap which operates in the following manner. Condensate enters at A and leaves at G; B is the

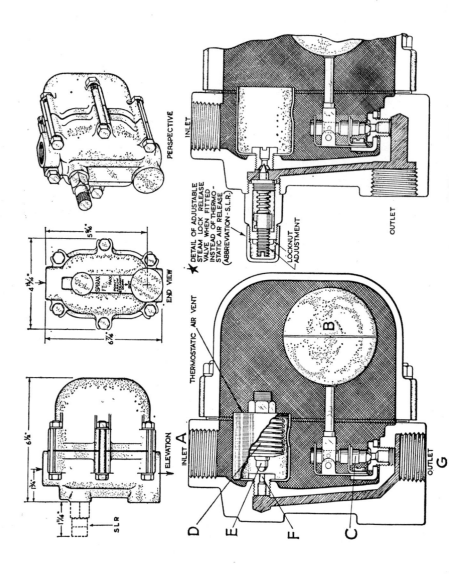

PERSPECTIVE

INLET

OUTLET

★ DETAIL OF ADJUSTABLE
STEAM LOCK RELEASE
VALVE WHEN FITTED
INSTEAD OF THERMO-
STATIC AIR RELEASE -
(ABBREVIATION - S.L.R.)

LOCKNUT
ADJUSTMENT

END VIEW

5⅝

4⅜

6⅞

ELEVATION

6⅞

1¾

1¹⁄₁₆

S.L.R.

THERMOSTATIC AIR VENT

INLET A

B

OUTLET G

D

E

F

C

hollow float which operates valve C; D, E and F together comprise a thermostatic air vent, D being the element which closes valve E on seat F. When the steam is first introduced to the plant, it must completely displace the air which has seeped into the pipes and traps during the shut-down period. Since valve E is free of seat F the air escapes freely until steam arrives, when element D expands and closes the valve. When condensate enters, it builds up in the body of the trap, raises the float and lifts valve C off its seat, thus allowing the condensate to be discharged.

In positioning a steam trap, it should be remembered that water collects at the lowest point of a pipe system. Convenience of access to the trap should never be permitted to overrule this.

Another method of condensate discharge employs a temperature-sensitive bulb and diaphragm-operated valve, in a manner similar to the temperature control system described on p. 201.

Since condensate consists of pure water and is normally hot, it is usually returned to a 'hot well' from which it is pumped into the steam-raising boiler and re-used.

Measurement of Temperature

The hand is often used to give some indication of the temperature of mill or calender rolls, but it can be misleading and is not to be generally recommended.

For ordinary air or liquid temperatures the mercury-in-glass thermometer is widely used, in either its laboratory form or shielded for factory use. There is also a form which has a specially reinforced bulb with a pointed end, very useful for taking the temperature of rubber in the mass, e.g. rubber dumped from an internal mixer or 'dollies' of rubber rolled off a mill. The principle employed in the mercury-in-glass thermometer is the change in volume with change in temperature of a quantity of mercury contained in a small glass bulb. This bulb leads to a tube of very fine and uniform bore (a 'capillary' tube) graduated in divisions which bear a definite relationship to two fixed points, the freezing point and boiling point of pure water at sea level.

On workroom temperature the Factories Act has this to say, "A reasonable temperature has to be obtained in each workroom. 'Reasonable' will depend upon the type of work carried out. A lower temperature is required for heavy physical work than for sedentary occupations. Where a substantial proportion of the work is done sitting, a temperature of at least 60° F must be obtained after the first hour. A thermometer must be provided in each such workroom." For reasons which have been discussed in Chapter VI, and quite unconnected with the comfort of the work-people, it is inadvisable to permit the temperature of any workroom in which unvulcanised rubber or uncured rubber products are stored, ever to drop much below 65° F. The thermometer required by the Factories Act is usually a cheap but adequate alcohol-in-glass type in a boxwood frame, on the front of which is marked the temperature scale.

Mercury-in-glass thermometers, whether shielded or not, are apt to be broken rather easily, and a more robust type, based on a different principle, is becoming popular. This is the 'Rototherm', the actuating element of which is strips of two metals rivetted together and wound in the form of a coil. The metals comprising this bi-metallic strip have different coefficients of expansion, and heating of the strip causes a turning movement which is transmitted to a pointer travelling over a calibrated dial.

The thermo-electric effect is an even more widely used principle in factory instruments for measuring temperatures. When two dissimilar metals are joined together and the junction heated, a small electric current is generated in the circuit (Fig. 58). The amount of this current is proportional to the difference in temperature between the hot junction and the cold end of the circuit. Such an assembly of two dissimilar metals, usually in the form of wires, is termed a 'thermocouple'. In practice the circuit has two junctions — the hot junction which is exposed to the temperature to be measured, and the cold junction which is kept at a standard temperature. The current produced is measured by a galvanometer and the temperature of the hot junction may be read from a calibration curve. The calibration curve, in this instance, is a graph showing the relationship between known temperature conditions at the hot junction of the thermocouple and the voltage in the circuit. By locating the thermocouple

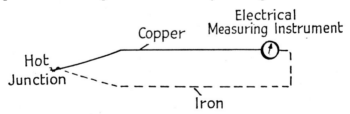

FIG. 58.   Thermo-electric circuit.

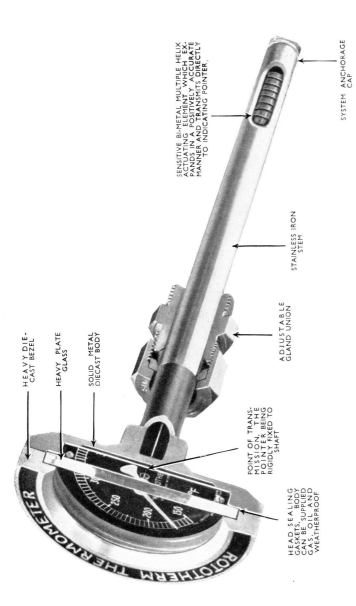

SENSITIVE BI-METAL MULTIPLE HELIX ACTUATING ELEMENT WHICH EXPANDS IN A POSITIVELY ACCURATE MANNER AND TRANSMITS DIRECTLY TO INDICATING POINTER.

SYSTEM ANCHORAGE CAP

STAINLESS IRON STEM

ADJUSTABLE GLAND UNION

HEAVY DIE-CAST BEZEL

HEAVY PLATE GLASS

SOLID METAL DIECAST BODY

POINT OF TRANSMISSION, THE POINTER BEING RIGIDLY FIXED TO SHAFT

HEAD SEALING GASKETS, BODY CAN BE SUPPLIED GAS, OIL AND WEATHERPROOF

ROTOTHERM THERMOMETER

Fig. 59.   Rototherm Principle

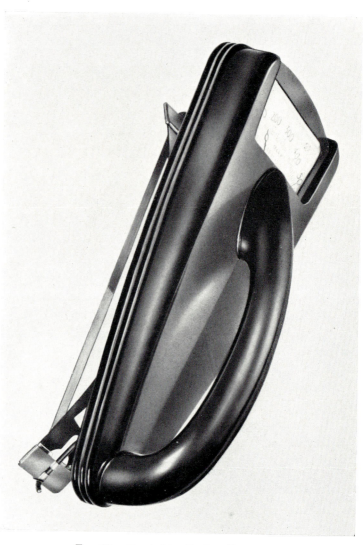

FIG. 60.   Cambridge Surface Pyrometer.

at a point where we wish to find the temperature and reading the voltage, the graph enables us to read off the unknown temperature. The most convenient factory instrument is one which has an automatically-compensated cold junction and a galvanometer reading directly in temperature degrees.

The thermo-electric principle is used in the Cambridge 'Surface Pyrometer' and similar instruments for the determination of temperatures of mill and calender rolls, press platens, etc. The temperature-sensitive element consists of a thin strip of metal with the junction of the two dissimilar metals at its middle. This flexible strip conforms to the contour of calender roll, mould surface, press platen, etc., and the temperature is read on a scale at the front of the instrument.

A needle pyrometer (a hypodermic needle with the two dissimilar wires fitted inside) can use the same recording instrument as for the 'Surface Pyrometer'. A needle thermocouple is particularly useful in checking tyre temperatures, temperatures of banks of rubber on mills, etc. A thermocouple may also be built into an article such as a tyre or conveyor belt and the progress of the transfer of heat followed throughout the cure.

Another method of temperature measurement, used not so much for direct reading as for recording and controlling temperature, is to employ a liquid-filled bulb as the sensitive element. The liquid is extremely sensitive to changes of temperature over the range for which the bulb is designed. The vapour pressure of the liquid is directly dependent on the temperature and therefore rises and falls with variations in the surrounding temperature. These changes in pressure are transmitted along a capillary tube to a flat, helically-wound steel tube, which winds and unwinds with changes in temperature and moves a pen-arm over a chart (Fig. 61).

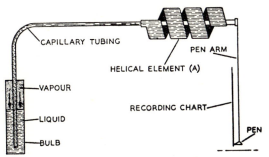

FIG. 61. Vapour pressure thermometer system.

An approximate idea of the temperature of a surface may be obtained by the use of temperature-sensitive paints, which change colour according to their temperature. These have only a limited application in the rubber industry. Certain chemical substances which have a sharp melting point are marketed in crayon-like form, the range of temperatures covering those most used by tyre retreaders and repairers. A mould surface may be quickly checked by stroking the surface with the appropriate crayon and noting whether or not the smear melts.

The Control of Temperature

One of the simplest ways of controlling temperature is to use a 'thermostat', a device which may employ a bi-metallic strip as already described in the 'Rototherm' thermometer. Due to the different co-efficients of expansion of the metals, heating of the strip causes movement in one direction which operates a switch to cut out the heating elements; cooling of the strip results in movement the other way which brings the heaters back into circuit. A thermostat may be set to cut in or out at any temperatures within its range.

Where steam is the heating medium, approximate control of temperature may be obtained by using a reducing valve to control the steam pressure. Reducing valves are spring-loaded devices which may be adjusted to give a desired pressure reduction, but they have the disadvantage that the controlled pressure may vary somewhat according to the variations in the pressure source.

A much more widely used method of controlling temperature is to use diaphragm-operated valves in place of the usual hand-operated steam stop valves. The up and down motion of the valve spindle, and therefore the opening and closing of the valve, is not done by hand but by the movement of a flexible diaphragm actuated by air pressure. The body of the valve is similar to that of the ordinary steam stop valve, but the top of the spindle bears on the rubber diaphragm and a spring returns the spindle to its original position when the air pressure is turned off. The air pressure on the diaphragm is controlled by the temperature variations in the tank or autoclave to which the system is fitted.

One of the many ways of effecting this control is shown in Fig. 62. 15 p.s.i. air pressure is needed for operation. The temperature-sensitive bulb is filled with a liquid which will develop a vapour pressure suitable for the range of temperature which is to be controlled.

When the temperature is being held at the specified figure, the bulb liquid is partly vaporised and the capsular spring is expanded just sufficiently to hold the ball of the air-valve at an intermediate position. Some air is discharging from the port at the air-valve ball pin, the remainder is passing to the diaphragm valve and throttling the steam supply sufficiently to maintain the temperature as desired. If the temperature rises, the vapour pressure of the liquid in the bulb

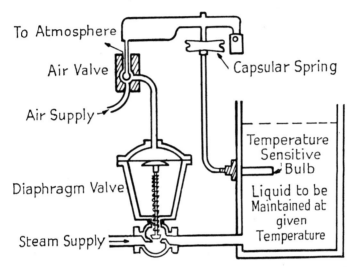

FIG. 62.   Typical temperature control system.

rises, the capsular spring extends further, pulling the air valve ball right up, thus allowing no air to escape through the discharge port. The full 15 p.s.i. air pressure passes to the diaphragm and closes the steam inlet valve. The opposite happens when the temperature falls; the ball valve shuts the air inlet, the top of the diaphragm is open to atmosphere and the spring on the valve spindle opens the steam inlet.

In the Bristol 'Free Vane' type of controller, the capsular spring is operated by air pressure which is varied by the movement of a thin metal vane, free to move between two opposing jets of air. The vane itself changes its position in relation to the jets as the result of the movement of a temperature-sensitive element actuated by a liquid-filled bulb.

The use of diaphragm valves can illustrate a principle which should be kept in mind in all forms of 'process control' — here we use the phrase in the instrument technologist's sense and not as in Appendix B. All control systems should be arranged to 'fail-safe' or 'fail to safety' , i.e. in the event of the failure of an instrument, or of the control air supply, the system should shut itself down. In a diaphragm valve the spring return can be arranged either to open or close the valve, as required by the operating conditions.

Time Cycle Controllers

The rubber industry uses many forms of these controllers. All that is required of the operative is that he push a button and this sets in motion quite a complicated series of operations.

A simple time cycle controller illustrates further uses of diaphragm valves, in this case supplying air and not steam to various parts of the mechanism. In one system an electric motor drives a metal disc or cam, the outer circumference of which is stepped in a manner to suit the desired cycle of operations. As the cam turns, a pointer in contact with the outer circumference follows the cam contour, and actuates a lever bar. This bar contacts in turn a series of tappets each connected to an air-valve, which controls the air pressure on the top of the diaphragm of the corresponding diaphragm valve, which then supplies high pressure air for carrying out the particular movement desired. It may, for instance, carry out the movement by acting on a plunger inside an air cylinder. The moulding of inner tubes is a good example of the application of time cycle control. The controller carries out, in correct sequence, the operations of closing and locking the mould, inflating an air-bag (which holds the mould faces shut tight), supplying the inflation air to the inside of the inner tube itself and, towards the end of the cure, exhausting this inflation air and then carrying out the first set of operations in reverse order.

Miscellaneous

We have now covered the main topics of instrumentation, but the student should also be acquainted with the following miscellaneous points.

The presence of excess moisture in rubbers and textiles can give rise to a variety of processing difficulties. Although the determination of the moisture content of materials will normally be carried out by laboratory personnel, the technician should know how to use the instruments for finding the 'humidity' (the amount of water vapour present in the air of the factory). In the wet and dry bulb system, two thermometers are mounted side by side in a housing which may be either stationary or whirled around by hand. One thermometer reads the air temperature, the other is surrounded by a wick kept moist from a little reservoir of water and, because of the evaporation of water from the bulb, gives a lower temperature reading. If the surrounding air is dry the water on the wet bulb will evaporate faster; if the air is pretty well saturated with water vapour, evaporation will be much slower. The humidity is found by taking wet and dry bulb readings and consulting a set of tables.

In winding up rolls of textile material it is often important to keep the edge straight. One type of web guide uses a photo-electric principle in which a beam of light controls an electric current. As the edge of the fabric wanders, the light beam is interrupted and electricity passed to a small motor which pulls the edge back to position. The principle is also used to control fabric 'accumulators' or 'festoons', the driving mechanism being switched off or on according to the presence or absence of a loop of the material in the path of the light beam.

Some mechanisms may use a micro-switch, one which requires only a very tiny movement to operate it; others employ mercury-switches, in which the tilting of the switch makes or breaks the circuit as the liquid metal bridges the electrodes.

You will recall that in Chapter VIII we discussed the effect of altitude on the accepted equivalence of steam pressure and temperature, e.g. at the altitude of Mexico City the temperature of steam at a pressure of 40 p.s.i. is only 282° F instead of the sea level temperature of 287° F. The effect of reduced pressure on the boiling point of water is usually demonstrated in the science classroom by heating water in a glass flask. Once the water is boiling vigorously the flask is tightly stoppered, immediately inverted and cold water poured over it. The cooling causes the steam to condense to water and the consequent reduction in pressure allows the water to 'boil' again at a reduced temperature. A spectacular demonstration of the pressure of the atmosphere is given by performing the same experiment with a petrol tin or similar vessel. In this case the comparatively thin walls of the tin are crushed inwards by the pressure of the atmosphere. In an industrial process using steam for heating, provision should be made to permit equalisation of internal and external pressures as cooling takes place. If this is not done the metal drums of, say, a fabric-drying machine may suffer the fate of the petrol tin. Automatic adjustment of the pressures may be effected by fitting an anti-vacuum valve. This is a spring-loaded device which opens when the internal pressure falls below that of the atmosphere. The astonishing power of atmospheric pressure should be kept in mind by the technician since it can explain

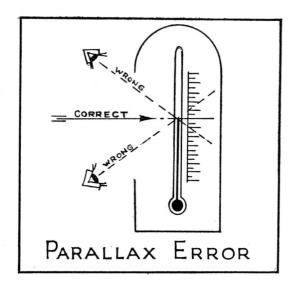

FIG. 63.

many apparently unrelated phenomena — difficulty of condensate removal from jacketed vulcanising pans, collapse of tyre curing bags at week-end shut-downs, etc.

It is customary nowadays to position all the instruments relating to a particular operation on a console or panel where they may be conveniently read by the operative. Where this is not done the pipe-fitter often places the thermometers and pressure gauges to suit the pipework with, unfortunately, little regard to convenience in reading. Further, the instruments are usually set at right angles to the pipe-work where it may be difficult to obtain an accurate reading due to 'parallax' error. This error may be introduced in any measurement in which a graduated scale is used. It can be avoided by having the eye vertically opposite the point on the scale which is being read. In the case of pressure gauges and thermometers the eye must be in line with the scale and respectively the pointer or the top of the mercury column. Some instruments are fitted with mirrors beneath the scales and the eye is in the correct position for reading when the pointer exactly covers its image in the mirror.

REFERENCE

MILLER, J. T., *A Course in Industrial Instrument Technology*. London

EXAMINATION QUESTIONS

The City and Guilds of London Institute holds examinations in Rubber Workshop Practice at two stages, Section 1 being taken after a two year course of study and Section 2 after a third year.

At each stage the examination consists of a written paper and a practical examination. For both Section 1 and Section 2, the written paper contains two types of questions, (a) a number of questions (usually about 15) to be answered in a few words, and (b) a smaller number of the more traditional type of question. About one hour is spent on the 'short answer' section and twenty minutes on each question in the other section.

In this Appendix, Part A contains some typical short questions and Part B the normal length questions. In Part C the questions require much the same time as those in Part B but they are somewhat more searching.

PART A

1. What property of rubber is responsible for giving it the name 'rubber'?
2. What is the precise meaning of the word 'synthetic'?
3. With what developments in the rubber industry are any three of the following associated: H. N. Ridley, C. Macintosh, R. W. Lunn, F. H. Banbury, T. Hancock, J. B. Dunlop, P. Schidrowitz, K. Ziegler, G. Natta?
4. What was 'Hancock's pickle'?
5. Why is 'ribbed smoked sheet' so called?
6. What is Para rubber?
7. What is air-dried sheet?
8. What is meant by the term 'modulus' as applied to a rubber compound?
9. What is the scientific name for the 'perishing' of rubber?
10. On what machine is the operation of profiling carried out?

11. What is an 'apron' mill?
12. What is the object of blending rubber?
13. What is meant by the 'scorching' of rubber? Give two other names for this effect.
14. What is a masterbatch?
15. Why is it necessary for the average rubber factory to carry different grades of masticated rubber?
16. Distinguish between 'latent' and 'sensible' heat.
17. What is a 'step' cure?
18. For what purposes do we use self-curing rubber mixes?
19. If a conveyor belt takes 5·5 sec. to travel 10 ft., what is its speed in yards per minute?
20. What ingredients comprise the curatives in a natural rubber compound?
21. What are the objects of using 'insoluble' sulphur in a rubber mix?
22. What is an antiozonant?
23. What are the three principal methods of manufacturing carbon black?
24. Explain the terms 'pure gum' mix and 'loading' of a mix.
25. What does the 'denier' of a yarn indicate?
26. In textile technology the word 'count' has two meanings. What are they?
27. What is meant by 'tendering' of a fabric?
28. Name two uses for conductive rubber.
29. How is hose distinguished from tubing?
30. State the 'Principle of Archimedes'.
31. What is the speediest method of determining the specific gravities of large numbers of samples of rubber?
32. Define 'specific gravity'.
33. LTP and OEP are types of SBR. Explain these abbreviations.
34. What is 'liquid' rubber?
35. What is a running nip?
36. To what rubber machinery are the 'Lunn principles' applied?
37. The temperature of certain workshops must be at least 60° F after the first hour of working. What is this temperature on the Centigrade scale?
38. What is meant by the phrase 'a scale of $1\frac{1}{2}$ in. to 1 ft.'?
39. What is the object of 'lagging' steam pipes?
40. What is a thermocouple?

Part B

1. Discuss the reasons which led to the foundation of (*a*) the plantation rubber industry and (*b*) the synthetic rubber industry.
2. Describe the preparation of First Latex Crepe, giving the precautions necessary to preserve the light colour.
3. Explain what is meant by the 'compounding' of rubber. State why such a procedure is necessary.
4. What is the purpose of masticating rubber? State the various methods available and give a detailed description of one of them.
5. Discuss the importance of the control of (*a*) the plasticity and (*b*) the scorch rate of a rubber compound.
6. What is meant by Continuous Vulcanisation? Give a brief description of the manufacture of one product which is vulcanised in this way.
7. What is an accelerator? What are the advantages of a 'flat curing' type?
8. What is the function of carbon black in a rubber compound? Outline the various methods by which carbon black is produced.
9. Give the reasons for the combining of rubber with a textile material in so many products of the rubber industry. Describe briefly the process of weaving a 'plain weave' fabric.
10. What is a V-belt? Give a brief description of the method of manufacture.
11. What are the objects of concentrating latex? Outline the main methods used.
12. What is a plastometer? Describe the main types and give details of the operation of one instrument with which you are acquainted.
13. Give the names of the synthetic rubbers in bulk production at present. Select one and state how its processing differs from that of natural rubber.
14. Describe the recent developments in the safe operation of horizontal two-roll mixing mills.
15. What area of rubber sheet would be required to cover completely the outer surface of a closed cylinder 24 in. long by 14 in. diameter. Neglect overlaps but add $12\frac{1}{2}\%$ for uncured waste.
16. Inspection Dept. reports blooming of one edge of press-cured floor mats. Discuss how you would trace the source of this defect. How would you correct the faulty mats?

17. What are lagging materials? Give examples and discuss the properties desired in such materials.

18. What is the main purpose of the Factories Acts? Give the headings of the various Sections and explain why it is essential for all supervisors to be acquainted with the provisions relating to his own particular job.

19. Distinguish between the 'thermo-electric' effect and the 'photo-electric' effect. Give examples of their uses in instrumentation and automatic control.

20. Why is it essential that a report should follow the solution of a factory problem? Outline the procedure in compiling such a report.

PART C

1. What is elasticity? To what is the elasticity of rubber due? On the basis of this theory, explain the difference between unvulcanised and vulcanised rubber.

2. What is Technically Classified Rubber? For what reasons was this type of rubber introduced?

3. What is Superior Processing Rubber? What types are available and in what ways are they superior in processing?

4. Discuss the disadvantages of the present methods of the manufacture of rubber products (latex to finished article). Can you indicate the possibility of any improvement in the near future?

5. Describe the use of conveyors in a rubber factory, stating advantages and disadvantages.

6. At what stages in rubber processing is premature vulcanisation likely to show itself? Outline the precautions you would take to minimise such trouble.

7. Describe the differences between compression, transfer and injection moulding, giving examples of products made by each method.

8. State the main groups into which compounding ingredients are divided. Write down the formula for any rubber compound you have mixed in the workshop, stating alongside the function of each ingredient.

9. Distinguish clearly between reclaimed rubber, mineral rubber,

P   C.R.T.

factice (rubber 'sub') and vulcanised rubber crumb. Indicate the use of each in rubber compounding.

10. Distinguish between 'man-made' and 'synthetic' fibres. Give a short account of the uses of such textiles in the rubber industry.

11. Taking 'dipped goods' as an example, discuss the relative merits of manufacture from latex and from solution.

12. In what ways does the design of a tubeless tyre differ from that of a conventional tyre? Describe the manufacture of the tubeless type (starting at the assembly stage) with particular reference to the tubeless features.

13. A cylindrical rubber bumper is 7 in. in outside diameter, 3 in. high, and has a 1 in. dia. central hole. Describe how you would determine the sp. gr. of the component without damaging it in any way. What would be the minimum press tonnage for moulding it by compression moulding?

14. Many rubber firms have recently entered the plastics field and, year by year, the two industries are drawing closer, both commercially and technically. Give a short account of the reasons for this development.

15. You are a proofing shop manager asked by your management to visit a disused factory in a country area and report on its suitability for conversion to a proofing section of the main factory. Address the report to your immediate superior, with your decision and reasons.

16. A rubber compound of sp. gr. 1·15 is calendered to $\frac{1}{16}$ in. thick, 18 in. width into polythene film 0·003 in. thick and weighing 0·125 lb. per sq. yd. What length in yards would be required to give a total weight (rubber and polythene) of 50 lb. ?

17. Give the main sources of technical information in the rubber industry, mentioning any periodicals with which you are acquainted. Explain why it is desirable that each organisation should have its own technical information service.

18. The present tendency in industry is to replace intermittent or 'batch' processes by a continuous flow of production. Discuss the advantages and disadvantages of this tendency in relation to the rubber industry.

19. During World War II the rubber industry suffered severe shortage of many raw materials. Discuss the developments of the last ten years which would minimise these difficulties in the event of future isolation of the U.K.

20. Many products of the rubber industry are required to be air-tight, vacuum-tight or to withstand fluid pressure. Describe the tests which are made to ensure that these products comply with requirements, and suggest any improvements in testing methods you would like to make.

BASIC LIBRARY AND READING LIST

The student is advised to purchase the books listed in the 'Basic Library'; the cost is not high and they provide answers to many questions for which there has been no room in the text. The 'Reading List' is a selection of the most important rubber literature published within the last ten years or so. Your College teacher or Works Librarian should be consulted before you contemplate purchase of these, since several are quite expensive.

BASIC LIBRARY

The Story of Rubber. Educational Productions Ltd., London

E. B. UVAROV and D. R. CHAPMAN, *A Dictionary of Science*. Penguin Books Ltd., Middlesex

KENNETH HUTTON, *Chemistry*. Penguin Books Ltd., Middlesex

L. S. POWELL, *Elementary Physics for Technical Students*. London

Handbook of Workshop Calculations. H.M.S.O., London

C. C. T. BAKER, *Practical Mathematics*. Vol. 1, London

A Guide to the Factories Acts, 1937–1959. National Joint Industrial Council for the Rubber Manufacturing Industry, Manchester

W. LONGLAND, *How to Read Workshop Drawings*. London

The student should have available for reference a good English dictionary, such as:

Chambers's Twentieth-Century Dictionary, New Mid-century Version

READING LIST: SCHOOL LEVEL

The Story of Natural Rubber, 8 page pamphlet   N.R.B.

Educational Kit, comprising

    (*a*) Book *Rubber in Story and Pictures*

    (*b*) Panel, Rubber Manufacture,

    (*c*) Panel, Rubber products in miniature,

    (*d*) Three wall charts on rubber production.

The Story of Rubber
Three wall charts — geographical significance, preparation of raw
    rubber, manufacture of rubber products.   E.P.

This is where rubber begins	D.R.C.
Story of the wheel	D.R.C.
Costume through the ages	D.R.C.
A short historical background of the rubber industry	D.R.C.
Making a car tyre	D.R.C.
Making footwear with rubber	D.R.C.
Making yourself comfortable	D.R.C.

TECHNICIAN AND JUNIOR TECHNOLOGIST LEVEL

The Fundamentals of Rubber Technology	I.C.I.
What every Engineer should know about Rubber	N.R.B.
Calenders for Rubber Processing	I.R.I.
History of the Rubber Industry	I.R.I.

SENIOR TECHNOLOGIST LEVEL

Applications of Science in Rubber Technology   I.C.I.
Rubber Technology — Lectures at RABRM Summer School, 1951
                Butterworth's Scientific Publications, London.

Ageing and Weathering of Rubber	I.R.I.
Reinforcement of Rubbers	I.R.I.

MANUFACTURE

What's in a Tyre	D.R.C.
Pneumatic Tyre Design	I.R.I.

The Story of Tire Beads and Tires
              McGraw-Hill Book Co., London.

Conveyor Belting	D.R.C.
Industrial Hose	Goodyear
Latex in Industry	R.A.N.Y.
Practical Latex Work	Blackfriars Press Ltd., Leicester.

Natural Rubber Latex and its Applications
    Nos. 1 to 5   N.R.B.
Machinery and Equipment for Rubber & Plastics Vols. I & II
    R. G. Seamen and A. M. Merrill   R.W.
Engineering Design with Rubber
    A. R. Payne and J. R. Scott   Maclaren
Engineering with Rubber   McGraw-Hill Book Co., London.
Rubber to Metal Bonding   Crosby Lockwood & Son Ltd., London.

REFERENCE

Rubber; Natural and Synthetic   H. J. Stern   Maclaren
Chemistry of Natural and Synthetic Rubber
   H. L. Fisher   Chapman & Hall, London.
Introduction to Rubber Technology
   M. Morton   Chapman & Hall, London.
Synthetic Rubber
   G. S. Whitby, Editor-in-Chief.
                                       Chapman & Hall, London.
Vanderbilt Rubber Handbook 1948 and 1958 Editions
                   R. T. Vanderbilt Co. Inc. New York, U.S.A.
Annual Report on the Progress of Rubber Technology   I.R.I.
Rubber Reviews (Rubber Chemistry & Technology)   A.C.S.
Rubber Trade Directory of Great Britain   Maclaren
Rubber Red Book   R.A.N.Y.
Analysis of Rubber and Rubber-like Polymers
   W. C. Wake   R.A.P.R.A.
The Technique and Practice of Costing for the Rubber Manufacturing
   Industry   F.B.R.A.M.
Glossary of Terms relating to Rubber and Rubber-like Materials
                                                         A.S.T.M.
Applied Science of Rubber
   W. J. S. Naunton, Editor.   Edward Arnold Ltd., London.

PERIODICALS

Rubber and Plastics Weekly   Weekly   Maclaren
Rubber & Plastics Age   Monthly
                                  Rubber & Technical Press,
                                  Gaywood Ho., Gt. Peter St.,
                                  London, S.W.1.
Rubber World   Monthly   R.W.
Rubber Age   Monthly   R.A.N.Y.
Rubber Abstracts   Monthly   R.A.P.R.A.
Transactions and Proceedings   Bi-monthly   I.R.I.
Rubber Developments   Quarterly   N.R.B.
Rubber Chemistry and Technology   Quarterly   A.C.S.

Here are the full addresses of the organisations referred to by initials above.

A.C.S.	American Chemical Society, Washington D.C., U.S.A.
A.S.T.M.	American Society for Testing and Materials, Philadelphia, U.S.A.
D.R.C.	Public Relations Dept., Educational Section, Dunlop Rubber Co. Ltd., 10–12 King St., London, S.W.1.
E.P.	Educational Productions Ltd., 17 Denbigh St., London, S.W.1.
F.B.R.A.M.	Federation of British Rubber & Allied Manufacturers, 19–20 Berners St., London, W.1.
Goodyear	Goodyear Tyre & Rubber Co. Ltd., Wolverhampton, England.
I.C.I.	Imperial Chemical Industries, Dyestuffs Division, Hexagon House, Blackley, Manchester 9, England.
I.R.I.	Institution of the Rubber Industry, 4 Kensington Palace Gardens, London, W.8.
Maclaren	Maclaren and Sons Ltd., Davis House, 69–77 High St., Croydon, Surrey.
N.R.B.	Natural Rubber Bureau, Market Buildings, Mark Lane, London, E.C.3.
R.A.P.R.A.	Rubber and Plastics Research Association of Great Britain, Shawbury, Shrewsbury, Shropshire, England.
R.A.N.Y.	Rubber Age (New York), Palmerton Publishing Co. Inc., New York 1, N.Y., U.S.A.
R.W.	Rubber World, Bill Brothers Publishing Co., New York, U.S.A.

INDEX